Medical School Interviews
All You Need To Know

The
Knowledge

D1634632

Dr. Mona Kooner

First Published 2012
by SPH Publishing

© Dr. Mona Kooner 2012

ISBN 978-0-9572904-0-2

Typeset by Shore Books and Design,
Blackborough End, Norfolk PE32 1SF

Printed and bound by the MPG Books Group, Bodmin and King's Lynn

Contents

Introduction

This book is for all those applying to medical schools in the U.K. Getting into a medical school is highly competitive and the interview is the final hurdle before applicants receive an offer. About half all candidates called to interview will get an offer. It often seems to applicants that the interview process involves an enormous amount of luck because the questions seem so random and infinite in variety. This is not true!

The interview is the chance you have to prove what you have said on your Personal Statement; to show the interviewers that you are an exceptional but well rounded and caring person whose enthusiasm and interest in Medicine has led to knowledge about medical matters. This book provides you with an understanding of the interview process and how your answers might be scored. It also gives you a lot of information on commonly asked subjects. The knowledge contained in this book is greater than would be usually expected from a medical school applicant. It is designed to prepare you for your medical school interview so you can impress and arouse your interest. However it is an easy read that omits unnecessary jargon and words.

I am a practising GP, GP tutor and as a senior doctor have been involved with interviews. I am also a Master NLP Practitioner [which teaches language, communication and behavioural skills] so I suppose combining Medicine and interview training was a natural progression. After helping a number of students I have realised that many despite enthusiasm have little idea of what is expected of them and the importance of background reading and research. I thought about how I could help and came up with what I call the Big Six aspects that form the elements of the medical school interview.

1. Why you want to become a doctor, your understanding of what medicine entails, your work experience and knowledge of medical subjects such as the structure of the NHS and the role of the GMC.

2. What is on your Personal Statement – your commitment to people, charity work, extra-curricular activities.

3. Competence based questions – 'tell me about a time when you showed; organisational/leadership/teamwork skills/how to handle mistakes and similar questions.'

4. Your attitudes – ethics and how to handle ethical scenarios.

5. Why do you want to come to this medical school?

6. Communication skills – how to present yourself.

This format has worked well. I have a number of medical colleagues, some of whom are interviewers and talking to them has been helpful. I ran a trial interview course with spectacular results. The course booklet seemed to have 'done the rounds' and was passed onto others with a number of people asking if they could buy one. This led to the idea of producing a book. I hope it will help you.

Dr Mona Kooner
MBBS [London] MRCGP DRCOG Master Practitioner NLP

Chapter 1

Understanding The Interview

What are interviewers looking for – what is on the mark schemes?

Entry into medical school is of course extremely competitive. Becoming a doctor is the dream of many but the privilege of only a few. The medical school interview is usually the final hurdle before getting the prize – an offer. About fifty percent of candidates called to interview will get an offer. I believe that there is a lot you can do to make sure you are among that fifty per cent.

By the time you have been called up to interview you will have shown by your GCSEs, AS levels, the UKCAT and the BMAT tests, your personal statement and references that you have the academic abilities to be a doctor. The interviewers know that you are academically suitable. Many interviewers are told to ignore UCAS points and GCSE results and to **solely evaluate applicants on other skills.** Well, what are these other skills? Below are some quotes from Medical School prospectuses. At interview they are looking for:

The Knowledge

Virtues of:

'Honesty, integrity, probity, steadfastness, courage, compassion, humility and empathy'.

'An appreciation of the human story, scientific knowledge and practical application that is involved in medicine'.

'Proven commitment to and the knowledge of the reality of becoming a doctor'.

'A commitment to people/community'.

'Good communication skills'.

'Ability to excel in non academic area, Evidence of leadership skills and team work'.

How do they assess the above qualities? **By what you say, examples you give and your general enthusiasm and knowledge.**

There is enormous pressure on medical schools to show that they are making **objective assessments** of candidates, not just subjective assessments. All will issue advice to those interviewing candidates and many will have mark schemes. It is now possible to ask for feedback from many universities so they need to have ways of justifying their actions.

The Knowledge

What will they ask me?

Although virtually anything can be asked you are **almost certainly** going to be assessed on the **big 6** below, and they will assess number 6 - your communication skills, while you answer questions throughout the interview.

1. **Your reasons for wanting to become a doctor** and your understanding of medicine, your work experience and your knowledge of medical subjects. E.g. the NHS, medical history, books and journals you have read

2. **Your personal statement;** commitment to people – charity work etc and your extra curricular activities.

3. **Competence based questions** – testing your skills, 'tell me about a time when you showed; organisational/leadership/ teamwork/ good communication skills/ ability to handle mistakes etc.'

4. **Your attitudes** i.e. your ethics. Most medical schools will give you an ethical scenario to talk through and test your values through other questions such as competence based questions.

5. Why you want to come to this medical school?

6. Your **communication skills** and interpersonal skills

The Knowledge

Although medicine is generally the most competitive course world wide, it is widely acknowledged that you don't have to be a genius to be a good doctor by those in the medical profession. Bright –and with a good memory yes but they already know that from your Personal Statement and UCAS form. In fact many great brain boxes such as Einstein and Leonardo Da Vinci had character traits which may have meant they would have been terrible doctors. **The interview is there to assess whether you have the personality to make a good doctor.**

Body Language

The now famous research paper by Professor Mehrabian of UCLA showed that 7% of feelings interviewers have about you are derived from the message conveyed by your words, 38% by the quality of your voice [tonality] and a massive 55% through gestures, expression and posture.

Impressions count. Your ability to build rapport with the interviewer and your words, image and speech working in harmony is important. If you say you are enthusiastic but sound dead bored you will come across as dishonest. Peoples' perceptions of your sincerity come from not what you say but **how you say it.** It also affects your likeability.

People feel rapport with people they feel they can relate to – people like them. Be aware of and to an extent match and model their tone, the loudness of their voice and body language [within reason]. If someone is talking quietly don't talk too loud. To an extent we all do this naturally when relaxed and receptive.

Arrive early, dress formally but in something you do not feel too uncomfortable. If you are not used to wearing a suit then formal trousers, shirt and tie will do but a suit is generally better. Girls should not wear anything revealing and keep jewellery to a minimum.

Start thinking about how you want to come across in advance of your interview and practise, practise, practise! Be aware of how you sit and of any little tics that come to the surface when you're under pressure (hair twiddling, hand wringing, eyebrow rubbing, nose twitching…). Videoing yourself is relatively easy nowadays and is worthwhile doing. You may find out that you do certain things subconsciously or you may be pleasantly surprised!

It's difficult to completely stop habits you have formed over a lifetime, but having a plan for how you can casually switch out of these movements when you recognise them happening means they won't be a showstopper in interviews.

Practise adopting your open posture and using smooth hand gestures in your daily life, for example, when you're talking with friends meeting new people responding in discussion groups and sitting in lessons.

I would recommend you sit with both feet on the ground and your hands in your lap. Lean slightly forward [look keen], leaning back can make you seem bored or arrogant. If there is a desk in front you may wish to put your hands on the desk but don't lean too far forward or put your elbows on the table, this may subconsciously be felt to be aggressive by examiners.

Look at the examiner attentively when they talk to you. Look at the person who asked the question when replying, be careful not to stare, and move your gaze and look at the others occasionally. In Britain it is in general considered rude not to look at people when they talk to you but aggressive if you look at them constantly when replying. [In other cultures this is reversed!]

Pause thoughtfully before answering for a few seconds only. This allows you to get your thoughts together.

Answer the question straight away [indirect answers are annoying]. Then back it up with an example. When giving an example it should be about you – what you did.

Answers should be about 1 -1.5 min (if not interrupted). Research has shown that this is the optimum length. It feels right – long enough to convey enough information without becoming boring and long winded. This might not seem long but when you practise you will find a lot can be said in this time. Remember that a question that might seem to be asking for a simple answer is usually an invitation to talk about a subject in an interesting and enthusiastic way. For example if you are asked

'When did you last do any work experience?' you should not simply answer *'Six months ago.'* but *'Six months ago I saw a very interesting patient who had ....'*
Answers should contain about 3-4 points maximum. People get bored if any longer and you start to sound long winded and waffly. You should prepare answers to the commonest questions by listing 3-4 points. For example *'tell us about a book/article you have read'* - make sure you have a 3 or 4 point summary of the book/article.

Be prepared if you raise a point to widen the debate. In this way **you can have some control** and take the lead on what you get asked, so make points you can expand on if an examiner picks on them.

For example

Question   *'You worked in an old people's home I see. How did you find that?'*

Answer   [Point 1] remember- answer the question directly

I initially found it difficult. Some of the elderly had severe dementia and got very confused and easily agitated. I was also unsure of how to react and lacked confidence.

[Point 2]

I remember how one lady suddenly got up and shouted at me and hit the tray of tea I was carrying. It was a real shock.

[Point 3]

I read up about how to care for the elderly; The Alzheimer's Society had a really good website. This taught me that the elderly are easily confused. I should explain what I am doing all the time and remind residents that it is tea time and we drink tea at tea time and so on. I gained more confidence after reading it and took swear words and rudeness less personally. The website suggested making a memory book for patients to help orientate them. I tried this for one or two and enjoyed it very much.

The candidate will almost certainly be asked to explain what a memory book is as the next question and thus influences what question he gets asked.

He also shows that he has intelligence, enthusiasm and self motivation to find ways of improving his interaction with the elderly and had managed to make it personally rewarding.

How to discuss your motivation for wanting to become a doctor

Try to make your answer personal, perhaps talk about your work experience. It will make it stand out. Remember the quotes from medical schools at the beginning of the chapter – remember what they are looking for - compassion, human interest scientific knowledge, commitment to community [Remember these are on their mark scheme]. Make sure you show you have these sorts of qualities and prove it to them with examples perhaps from your charity work or Personal Statement.

What are the downsides of a career in medicine?

The interviewer is checking that you fully understand what medicine entails. Replies may include: 5-6 years as a student, a further 5-10 years of further training, unsociable long hours, earning relatively little until you are in your late 30s, life long learning and exams and revalidation, witnessing distressing deaths and illnesses, risking emotional and empathy burnout. Remember you are dealing with people at their most vulnerable and emotional – anger and complaints are common and not always deserved.

This was one of my favourite questions – I would want to

make sure that the interviewee had thought fully about the implications of being a doctor and realised what he/ she would be letting themselves in for. Looking at the career with seemingly 'rose tinted' glasses does not go down well.

Why a doctor and not something else?

Why not a scientist/nurse /physiotherapist?

Remember your interviewers are unlikely to be all doctors. Always be respectful of all professions. Most professions in the health service are 'caring' professions and have a scientific basis. It is reasonable to say however that:

'being a doctor would give me a greater understanding of how the body works compared to a nursing degree as it is a more academic and a longer course and this would suit me better.'

Or in response to *'Why not a scientist?'*

'I love science and understand that scientists are responsible for most medical progress but people fascinate me and I enjoy interacting with them. During my work experience ....'

Work Experience

'It is not the quantity or quality of a candidate's work experiences that matter but the insight and their ability to draw meaning from it'
Remember interviewers want to see evidence of enthusiasm, 'emotional intelligence', empathy and an ability to reflect on what has been seen. You are often asked a general question such as *'Tell me about your work experience'.* You won't impress by simply reeling a list of hospitals and consultants however impressive because it tells very little about your personal qualities. It is far better to talk in some detail about a particular patient and what you learnt about that case.

You are only likely to be asked about **one patient,** so know one patient and their illness *from each of the specialities you have had experience,* well. Use phrases like 'I found it very interesting so I went home and looked it up' to show your motivation. Make sure that you show your empathy when recounting the patient story and how the disease affects the patient. Try and make 3-4 points in total that show you have the qualities that they are looking for – **Intellectual ability, motivation and interest and empathy.**

E.g. *'While doing an attachment in neurosurgery I saw a patient with a frontal brain tumour. He was a 52 yr old man who had presented to his GP with early morning headaches and sudden 'out of character' depression. I was interested so I read up about brain tumours and found out that raised intracranial pressure due to the tumour causes early morning headaches and lesions in the frontal lobe cause personality changes.*

I was very moved by an article in the BMJ – 'A Patient's Journey' which described a lady with a tumour who became profoundly disabled after her operation, lost movement in her limbs and her speech. She described how her dreams were shattered and her marriage broke up and her little daughter rejected her and found seeing her too distressing. I worried about what kind of disability the patient I saw would be left with.

I learnt a lot about the multidisciplinary team and was surprised by the number of doctors from specialities ranging from radiology to anaesthetics and other health care professionals such as physiotherapists, O.Ts [occupational therapists] and psychologists who would help the patient after surgery.'

The above example shows that the candidate took the initiative and showed the enthusiasm to read about the patient and had read medical magazines. It shows that the candidate has compassion and empathy and had noticed and appreciated all the other professions. The third point, the multidisciplinary team may tempt the interviewers to ask about it and so **a well prepared student can exert some control over the questions asked by bringing in a related matter at the end.**

Commitment to community/teaching/ charity work

This is becoming increasingly important. Evidence of charity work is essential and some medical schools regard it as important as work experience. It is known that middle class children are more likely to obtain work experience than those coming from less privileged backgrounds but everybody can volunteer for such work. It shows a selfless caring personality.

Again use the 3 point summary method – say why you did it and what you learnt, how it helped you to become a better person and how it will help you to be a better doctor.
e.g.

'I was quite apprehensive about visiting the hospice. I had feared that it would be full of dying people in pain.

But the staff were so caring to patients and their relatives. There was a Carers Support Group and I became aware of the stress of being a carer. That they had to cope with an impending bereavement complicated medication regimes, machinery that kept bleeping and often had disturbed nights.

I read up about Dame Cecily Saunders and the hospice movement; she said that a hospice should provide for 'the physical, psychological and spiritual needs of a patient. I was deeply impressed by it all and would like to emulate the attitudes I experienced there when I am a doctor.'

Your personal statement

Know your personal statement better than the back of your hand. Look carefully at **each phrase** and think of what questions it could possibly lead to and prepare for them. If you mention stem cells – learn all about them and any recent developments and the arguments for and against their use. Again prepare! When you are asked about your achievements it can sound like boasting and many candidates feel uncomfortable recounting their achievements in this way, so back it up and always explain how it can help with a career in medicine; you will also sound more likeable if you explain that achievements did not come easily.

e.g. 'My rowing success has come as a result of many hours of practice. I row four times a week and get up at 7.00 am every Sunday morning even in the rain and cold. As well as the physical fitness I have developed qualities of self discipline and resolve. Like most teenagers I like my bed on a Sunday morning but these qualities will help me in a career in medicine.'

The candidate here also sounds more likeable because he explains that achievements did not come easily and reminds the interviewer of the amount of dedication and the hours that are needed to gain such an achievement.

Remember if you say you are a keen rugby player/cricket player etc and have said so on your Personal Statement **make sure you know what is happening in that sport** thoroughly. I have heard about interviews which seemed to be mainly about cricket!

Competency-based questions

To measure your suitability, interviewers may ask questions where you will need to draw on examples from your life so far to demonstrate times when you have employed particular competences. The logic is simple: your past ability to use a skill is a good indicator of your potential to be successful in the future.

These include:

Can you think of a time when team work was important?

Tell us about a project you have been involved in.

Have you ever made a mistake?

How do you handle conflict?

Tell me about your leadership skills.

With competency-based questions it is very easy to go off topic or meander around providing too much detail about the situation when the interviewer really wants to know how you acted. You may find it helpful to use the STARR approach to structure your response:

- **S**ituation: give the interviewer a context by describing the situation.

- **T**ask: what was your goal?

- **A**ction: tell the interviewer what your specific actions were.

- **R**esult: the end result – make sure it shows you in a good light, even if the overall project was not a success.

- **R**eflect – what you have learnt/ have you implemented any changes to ensure it wont happen again

E.g. – in response to: How do you handle conflict/Was there a time when you had to handle conflict?

[Situation] During our Duke of Edinburgh Gold expedition there was a disagreement between 3 members of the group and one boy who wanted to do certain things differently.

[Task] I wanted to get the group talking and working together again without any hard feelings

[Action] I spoke to the boy and listened to him. I said that I understood that he felt angry and hurt but that we all wanted the same thing at the end – a successful expedition and was there any compromise he could come up with which would put him in a favourable light?

[Result] He managed to come up with a generous compromise and was given credit by the group for being so adjusting.

[Reflect] I read that diplomacy 'is the art of creating ladders for people to climb down gracefully'. It seemed to work here.

Think of scenarios that would fit these answers to these questions before hand. You can sometimes use the same scenario to fit a number of questions. For example the above example could be adapted to answer both 'Can you tell us of a time when team work was important 'and 'Tell me about your leadership skills.'

Personal insight/honesty/probity

Interviewers want to 'weed out candidates' whom they feel might not have the above attributes. People who are high achievers often feel superior to others, are opinionated, find it difficult to admit they are at fault [it may happen rarely] and have narcissistic qualities; people with these traits can have a devastating impact in medicine. An extreme example, Harold Shipman a GP was convicted of being Britain's greatest mass murder having killed over 218 of his patients [but probably many more] in 2000. This and a much greater focus on why and how 'things go wrong' as in Mid Staffordshire Hospital have led to questions, MMIs and scenarios meant to test the probity and attitudes [ethics] of candidates.

This of course is not easy to determine but they may well try and test your honesty and questions about mistakes are common. The last Chief Medical Officer Liam Donaldson instituted many ideas to try and; reduce the number of medical mishaps [iatrogenic illnesses are the 3rd most common cause of death after cardiovascular disease and cancers]. He said:

'to err is to be human, not to apologise unforgiveable, to cover up criminal'.

Typical questions include;

Tell us about a time when you made a mistake.

Have you ever been wrong?

Have you ever had to change your mind?

How do you cope with criticism?

The Knowledge

Is there such a thing as positive criticism?

Do you have any weaknesses?

Recently a medical school had a MMI where candidates had to act out the following scenario.

'You are a baker and a customer has come to collect a birthday cake he says he ordered. There is no cake ready.'

Looking at the above quote from Liam Donaldson I am sure the mark scheme would look something like that below:

Does the candidate admit the fault?

Does he take responsibility?

Does he apologise?

Does he try to make up?

Does he try and institute a procedure to ensure it does not happen again?

Make sure you have an **example of a mistake,** make sure it is not too petty [eg I chose to do rugby rather than football] and that you learnt from it.

Have **a 'weakness' you can discuss** and say what you are doing about it. *'Discuss your strengths and weaknesses'* is a common question.

<u>Stress</u> *'How do you cope with stress?'* It is important to remember that a certain amount of stress can be good. It can drive us to attain. For example we probably would not learn so

effectively if we did not have the threat of exams which would test our knowledge. It is important for people to recognise when 'stress' is becoming unhealthy and take measures to combat it. These can include re evaluating how to manage a work load and ensuring ways of relaxing such as sports, music and friends. There is also never any shame in seeking advice. This question examines a candidate's personal insight.

Arrogance

There is nothing as off putting as a candidate who appears arrogant. Unfortunately nerves, which can make people self defensive and the desire to sell yourself and beat the competition can make people seem arrogant even if they are usually not. I have also heard it said that anyone who can write two hundred words about their achievements and talk for 20 minutes about how good they are at the age of eighteen is intrinsically obnoxious. Remember your interviewers know and have achieved so much more than you - treat them with respect. Humility is important.

Either or Questions

Do you prefer to work by yourself or in a team?

Is medicine a science or an art?

Are you a leader or a follower?

Be careful; these questions are not really asking you to choose between two options. Often the answer is both!

An example of an answer to 'Are you a leader or a follower' is;

'Both. I am happy to be a leader and to take the initiative and responsibility when required but I am equally happy being delegated to and playing my part as a member of a team.'

-then back your answer up with examples of team work and leadership skills.

Antagonistic Questions

Examiners often play devil's advocate and may sound as if they profoundly disagree with your answer. Do not be put off by this as it may be part of a deliberate strategy to see how you react under pressure. Flexibility and an ability to recognise and consider an alternative point of view is an important attribute.

For example, when a candidate was asked whether the morbidly obese should be allowed to have children he replied that one had to respect the autonomy of patients and not be judgemental. The examiner retorted – 'Yes but obese parents have obese children –they are not just harming themselves.' This threw the candidate who was then lost for an answer. It would have been better to acknowledge that point and to continue discussing both sides of the argument. E.g.

'Yes that is very true. However if you start to not allow obese people to have children then you could make a similar argument for all sorts of conditions such as alcohol abuse, smokers whose children end up as passive smokers. You could end up with a slippery slope at the bottom of which there were only a few vetted, potential parents. But it does raise a really interesting point and perhaps the fact that obese parents tend to have fat children could be used as leverage. For example if you told a mother that by improving her health and by exercising and making healthy meals for the family

[rather than just pizza and chips that the kids prefer] she is improving not just her health and chances in life but those of her children.'

Remember, **do not come across as opinionated**, consider the examiners point and examine both sides of the argument. If you are contradicted and shown to be **clearly wrong** about something it is **best to accept and acknowledge** it early on in a discussion.

What if I really can not think of an example?

Don't panic. Remember you are not expected to know everything. If you can not think of an example say so and perhaps try and offer an alternative. For example an interviewee was asked.

'Have you read about any ethical dilemmas in the press in the last couple weeks?' She could not think of any despite having read the medical press thoroughly. She could have said

'I have been reading newspapers and magazines but have not come across any in the last two weeks but the debate on assisted suicide is a common topic in the press ....'

It is more than likely that talking about assisted suicide instead would be acceptable.

Similarly a response to a question such as 'Tell me about somebody who has changed your life.'

If you can not think of anybody it would be best to say.

'I don't think I have had that experience as yet but there are plenty of people who have been very important influences. For

example my biology teacher….'

Nerves

Change perception nerves.

It is normal to be nervous but remember the best way to deal with nerves is **to feel prepared.** Nerves can actually help you perform better; actors talk about 'being fired up' and ready to go.' It is best to play the interview over in your mind beforehand, Professional sportsmen all use sports psychology and imagine the match and winning. So imagine the interview. Imagine it going well but not going perfectly, not being able to answer some tricky questions but able to pick up and keeping the interviewers' interest and impressing them overall.

Chapter 2

A Brief History Of Medicine And What The Future Holds

Medical history

Most medical schools say that you will be expected to have a layman's knowledge of medicine. Common questions include
- **'Tell me what do you think have been the most important advances in the last 200 /100/50/10 yrs?**
- **Who was Hippocrates?**
- **What do you think the most important medical advances will be in the next 50 yrs?**

The development of new treatments has always tested **ethical boundaries**. When anaesthesia was developed it was denounced as unnatural and that pain and suffering taught us important lessons. Later **blood transfusions** were rejected by some as again unnatural and playing God and many who belong to **the Jehovah's Witness Church** still refuse them and other treatments. The same arguments were used when organ transplants and IVF appeared on the scene.

Often you will be asked questions which test your understanding of important developments, so this chapter is meant to provide you with a basic knowledge.

Hippocrates

Hippocrates [370 BC] a Greek physician, has often been called 'the father of medicine.' He is most famous for the **Hippocratic Oath** which described **ethical principles** that a doctor should abide by. Many of these such as the concept of confidentiality and always acting in the best interest of the patient are still relevant and have been incorporated into modern day medicine. Examples of extracts of the original Hippocratic Oath include:

'Whatever houses I may visit, I will come for the benefit of the sick.'*[The principle of Beneficence]*

'What I may see or hear in the course of treatment or even outside of the treatment in regard to the life of men, which on no account one must spread abroad, I will keep myself holding such things shameful to be spoken about.' [*The principle of Confidentiality*]

Although doctors do not actually swear the Hippocratic Oath today, these ethical principles have been incorporated into medical ethics and the GMC has similar rules in its document Good Medical Practice [see section on GMC].

At the time of Hippocrates, it was common to blame disease and injury on the gods and attempts to treat the problem were done by prayer and by priests. By contrast, Hippocrates believed that disease was the **product of environmental factors and living habits**. He is considered the **first advocate of evidence-based medicine**. Rather than blaming illness on the supernatural, he used **reasoning and observation,** recorded findings and built on them. In addition, he kept medicine separate from the work of priests. The Hippocratic

School was also one of the first known to describe diseases and name them e.g. lung cancer.

Medicine in Roman times

Most of the doctors in Rome were Greeks. The greatest was **Galen.** He successfully treated the Emperor and became Rome's leading doctor. He gave lectures and wrote books which were used as the basis of western medicine for 1400 years after his death. He had dissected human bodies in Alexandria where it had been allowed and had an **impressive knowledge of anatomy**. However he supported the **theory of the four humors** i.e. that there were four main fluids in the body –blood, phlegm, yellow bile and black bile and that illness happens when there is an imbalance between these.

Although doctors had no real effect on the health of the population in Roman times, Romans realised the **importance of sanitation**. In AD 100 there were nine aqueducts to bring water to Rome, tanks to purify it and lead pipes to take it to houses of the rich and the public baths. In smaller towns and army forts throughout the Empire there were similar systems.

Vegetius a Roman writer wrote in the 4th century AD showing knowledge of the principles of public health:

Keeping the army healthy:

A soldier who must face the cold without proper clothing is not in a state to have good health or march. He must not drink swamp water. Daily exercise is better than the doctor for soldiers. If a group of soldiers is allowed to stay too long in one place in the summer or autumn they begin to suffer the effects of polluted water, and are made miserable by the smell of their own excrement. The air becomes unhealthy and they catch diseases. This has to be put right by marching to another camp.

Medicine up to the 1800s

When the Roman Empire collapsed the only strong organisation to survive was the Church. Its clergy could read Latin and kept the ideas of Galen alive and as it was a Christian duty to look after the sick the Church took over the running of hospitals. Faith, prayer and asking the help of saints were thought to be more effective than medical study. Public Health systems were forgotten and doctors and their treatments usually did more harm than good. During the epidemics of Bubonic Plague that drastically reduced the population of Europe, doctors became known as quacks because of the bill shaped mask that plague doctors wore to 'frighten away the plague' and protect themselves from the stench. The sort of treatments used usually made the patient worse. They were fond of blood letting [which would have unnecessarily weakened patients] and practised such things as putting frogs on buboes to rebalance the humors.

A plague doctor

Medical practice at this time was horrific. Treatments were brutal and usually made you worse. Operations invariably had to be carried out without anaesthesia and were performed by barbers who normally just cut hair and shaved people. [This is why surgeons to this day are called Mr – originally they were not learned doctors]. A visit to the Wellcome History of Medicine displays sights very similar to the torture chambers in Madame Tussauds or the London Dungeons.

Medicine and the Scientific Revolution

The scientific principles of detailed **investigation, experimentation, logic and proof** were beginning to have an effect in Britain. The work of Isaac Newton and **The Royal Society** had an effect on the thinking of the educated and in medical schools the training became more scientific. Doctors had to study anatomy, chemistry, botany and 'clinical observation' was introduced as a separate subject. The result was that doctors observed their patients more carefully and some applied their scientific training to what they saw. Microscopes became powerful enough by 1830 to see bacteria and the science of chemistry had advanced so that by 1770 oxygen had been discovered.

This all coincided with the **industrial revolution** which led to an enormous shift of people into towns with consequent overcrowding, poor sanitary conditions and disease. Small pox and cholera were rife and **life expectancy had** [which was now being measured by the Registry of Births Deaths and Marriages] **decreased**! In 1840 average life expectancy in one city for working class men was just 19! [as so many died when young]. The combination of worsening health and increasing scientific knowledge and application eventually led to change.

Great Medical Men of the 1700s and 1800s

Edward Jenner and vaccination

Jenner worked as a doctor in rural Gloucestershire but remained a fellow of the **Royal Society**. He took an interest in stories that suggested that milk maids had beautiful complexions because they never caught small pox. Small pox was a disfiguring disease that left skin pitted and scarred. He knew that milk maids often caught cow pox and had cow pox lesions [similar to small pox lesions] on their hands. **He hypothesised that having had cow pox you were likely to be resistant to small pox.** So in an experiment, which would be regarded as enormously unethical nowadays, he took some liquid from a cowpox lesion and injected it into a healthy eight year old boy called James Phipps. He later took some liquid from a patient with small pox and injected the liquid into James Phipps. James Phipps did not get small pox even when inoculated again with small pox several months later. Cow pox inoculation seemed to have given him permanent resistance to small pox.

Jenner repeated this study 23 times before publishing his results in a book in 1798 in which he described his results but gave no explanation why they worked. He met some resistance being only a country doctor but was helped by being a member of The Royal Society. He became world famous and was thanked by the King and given a fortune of £30,000 by Parliament. Thomas Jefferson the President of the USA personally wrote to him saying 'mankind will never forget that you have lived.'

Jenner wrote to Napoleon during war between England and France to secure the release of two English prisoners of war.

Napoleon is reputed to have said: "Ah, Jenner, je ne puis rien refuser a Jenner" ("Ah, Jenner, I can refuse him nothing").

The word **vaccination comes from 'vacca' meaning cow** because the first vaccine was developed from cows.

Chadwick

Edwin Chadwick was not a doctor; he was the secretary and close friend of Bentham a famous utilitarian. Utilitarianism believes in 'the greatest good for the greatest number of people'. Bentham founded University College London [his skeleton is still kept there].

After Bentham died Chadwick became Secretary of the Poor Law Commission and he became convinced that **sickness** was a major **cause of poverty**. He was sure that **sickness was caused by unsanitary conditions** and diligently collected data that proved this. He produced his 'Report on the Sanitary Conditions of the Working Population'. This alerted those in power to the extreme overcrowding and poor conditions which were causing life expectancy to fall.

Average age of death [rural]	In Manchester[urban]	Rutland
Professions, gentry and families	38	52
Tradesmen and their families	20	41
Labourers and their families	17	38

Taken from Chadwick's Report on the Sanitary Conditions of the Working Population.

He argued that central government should organise a **proper public health system**. Parliament set up a Board of Health in 1848 and Chadwick became a leading member. He organised further investigations and tried to force the cleaning up of areas and water. He suggested using hollow oval clay pipes to provide clean water and for sewage disposal, rather than the large square open pipes and drains.

'there were few privies [toilets] – some yards over 60 people have only one to use. Inside, the houses were worse –no running water, no drains, no proper ventilation…. Dr. Piper found 15 persons in two small rooms were ill at the same time with typhus fever.' [Report to the General Board of Health Darlington 1850]

Chadwick however was very unpopular and people disliked being ordered about by a civil servant. It was felt that people had a right to be unsanitary.

'The Board of Health has fallen ……There is nothing a man hates as much as being cleaned against his will, or having his floors swept, his walls white washed, his pet dung heaps cleared away, all at the command of a sanitary bumbaliff'

The Times 1st Aug 1854

Although Chadwick was defeated his ideas were taken up and he is often talked about as the father of Public Health. Even today Public Health is seen as perhaps the most important way of improving a population's health. **In third world countries dirty water and over crowding are still the cause of most deaths.** At the beginning of the 20th century **life expectancy increased rapidly because of public health measures**.

John Snow and the Broad Street Pump

Dr John Snow noted that a terrible **outbreak of cholera** took place in Broad Street, London 1854. However the workers of brewery on the street were not affected. They apparently did not drink water, only beer. Dr Snow thought that the water might be contaminated and plotted cases of cholera on a map; he noted that even outlying cases mentioned that they obtained their water from the Broad Street pump. He had the handle of the pump removed so people could not use it and cases of cholera fell. John Snow concluded that there was **something in the water that caused cholera**. This is thought to have been the first epidemiological study. **Epidemiology** is the branch of medical science dealing with the **transmission and control of disease**.

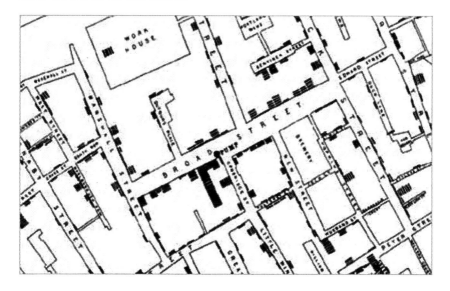

Dr John Snow's map

Although the Board of Health had been disbanded the Government was forced to react to '**the Great Stink of London**' [when sewage and noxious smells from the Thames had forced Parliament to close] and to cholera epidemics. **Dr John Simon was made the first Chief Medical Officer.** His further investigations backed up Dr John Snow's hypothesis that cholera was spread by water. He passed legislation that legislated for clean water, sewage disposal and overcrowding. John Snow also **formed the GMC** which undertook registration of medical practitioners and ensured standards.

Pasteur

The **miasma theory** of illness held that disease arose spontaneously. People like Chadwick believed that bad air or smells led to disease. Pasteur [a French chemist] showed **that micro -organisms were responsible for disease** and they did not arise spontaneously. He showed that micro-organisms were responsible for wine becoming sour. If samples were heated micro-organisms could be killed and things did not go bad. We still use **pasteurisation** today, for example milk is flash heated to prolong its life and ensure its safety. He believed in the **germ theory of disease** but could not prove that germs caused diseases in humans. Although he tried hard to find the germ that caused the cholera epidemics in Europe he failed. Robert Koch had that honour.

Robert Koch

Koch was a German doctor who had read of Pasteur's discoveries and found a way to stain cells so they could be seen. In 1887 he isolated the germ causing anthrax, then a few years later tuberculosis and in 1883 cholera. His discoveries led to the germ theory of disease being fully accepted. He is famous for **Koch's postulates** which stated that to prove that an organism is the cause of a disease the following must apply:

1. It must be found in all cases of the disease while being absent in healthy tissue

2. It can be isolated

3. It must be capable of producing the original infection even after several generations of culture.

4. It must be retrievable from an inoculated animal

He started the **speciality of microbiology**.

The germ theory of disease started to lead to more cures. Pasteur and his team produced a vaccine against anthrax then rabies. Koch's assistant Behring produced the first anti-toxin vaccination against diphtheria. He discovered that some germs produced poisons or toxins and some animals produce anti-toxins to fight these poisons.

Lister

Surgery was barbaric. It involved strapping and holding patients down while a surgeon did what was considered the necessary operation in as little time as possible. Surgeons would wear their dirtiest clothes – splattered with pus and blood as they did not want to spoil others. They had no understanding of how disease spread.

Lister was a Professor of Surgery at a time when most surgical operations ended with the death of the patient from post operative infections. He had read about Pasteur's work and the idea that germs caused disease and knew that carbolic acid had been used to treat sewage. So he tried carbolic acid as an **'antiseptic'** to kill germs. This resulted in an enormous improvement in the mortality rate.

Resistance to Lister's ideas was strong. It was hard to convince surgeons that tiny objects 0.001mm such as microbes could kill. Surgeons and their staff resented all the extra washing and work that Lister's methods entailed. One famous surgeon would always raise a laugh by telling anyone who came into the operating theatre to shut the door *'lest one of Mr Lister's microbes should come in'*. However results using antiseptics were very conclusive and Koch's germ theory of disease eventually provided an explanation. Soon other antiseptics were developed.

James Simpson and the invention of anaesthetics

In 1847 James Simpson, an Edinburgh obstetrician started to use chloroform this enabled patients to have virtually pain free operations. Dr Simpson and two of his friends used to sit together every evening and try new chemicals to see if they had an anaesthetic effect. One of the chemicals they tried was chloroform; on inhaling they described feeling cheerful but then suddenly collapsing only to regain consciousness the next morning. It took several years for Simpson and his friends to persuade others to use chloroform, especially in the field of obstetrics. It was thought by many that it was God's will that labour should be painful and that relieving pain was unnatural!

'The pain and sorrow of labour exert a powerful and useful influence upon the religious and moral character of women' Lancet 1853

However John Snow [of the Broad Street Pump] gave Queen gave Queen Victoria chloroform during the birth of her 8th child. The news spread and it became difficult for doctors to refuse requests for chloroform

Medicine in the 20th Century

Medicine entered the 20th century vastly different from the previous century. It was now based on science. Doctors were taught anatomy, encouraged to observe and experiment and record. There was a massive improvement in life expectancy because of Public Health improvements such as clean water. Vaccination and understanding of nutrition continued to reduce mortality rates. Surgery was more successful because of stricter hygiene and antiseptics. It was also less barbaric because of the arrival of anaesthesia. The GMC had been formed and regulated doctors.

Antibiotics and the successful fight against infectious diseases

The germ theory of disease had been accepted and the fight against infectious diseases became more successful as more vaccines were discovered. The first antibiotic called salvarsan, was discovered in 1909. In 1932 a group of antibiotics called sulphonamides were found to cure a range of infectious diseases. In 1928 Alexander Fleming [St Mary's Medical School, now part of Imperial College] noticed that a mould that had landed on a bacterial culture seemed to have killed those bacteria near it. He used 'mould juice' from this mould to treat mice that had been deliberately infected with a number of organisms. He also treated a colleague successfully without any complications. Fleming wrote up this discovery but did no more to develop it. He thought that it may have potential use as an antiseptic or lab reagent but no more. It was Professor Florey and Chain from Oxford who followed up Fleming's work successfully and managed to 'purify' the mould juice. By 1940 they had enough penicillin to test it properly and it worked spectacularly. There were heavy bombing raids on British cities and the Government was obliged to help its citizens and treat its soldiers and there was cooperation between the Allied Governments and the newly developed drug companies. This enabled penicillin to be mass produced. Other effective antibiotics were discovered and mortality from infectious diseases fell sharply.

The fight against infectious disease has been remarkable. It is no longer one of the largest three killers in this country. Anti-viral agents as well as antibiotics [anti-bacterial] agents have been developed. HIV infection usually meant an early death but now if treated early and with combination therapy patients can expect a normal life span. However widespread use of antibiotics has led to increasing antibiotic resistance i.e. bacteria which have developed mutations that make them unaffected by antibiotics have become more common. The use of broad spectrum antibiotics in hospital leads to the bacteria that are normally found on or in the body dying, leaving room for disease producing bacteria resistant to antibiotics to grow. **MRSA** [methicillin resistant staphylococcus aureus] is a multi resistant bacterium that is a major problem in hospitals. Proper hygiene, washing of hands and antiseptics are still important.

Imaging

Medicine develops mainly because of increased knowledge in the sciences. Teams responsible for advances include those from fields other than medicine. Major scientific advances in the 20th century include imaging. Wihelm Roentgen first used x-rays in 1895. X-rays quickly became popular and are enormously useful at looking at bones, teeth and foreign objects such as bullets. By 1970 most Americans were receiving at least one X-ray every year from physicians and dentists. However, it is now known that X-ray radiation can lead to the development of leukaemia and other cancers. X-rays should be used only when absolutely necessary. The destructive effects of radiation are sometimes used to treat cancer in the speciality of radiotherapy.

Ultrasound started to be used after World War Two and by the 1970's other imaging machines such as CAT scans and MRI scanners were developed. Unlike x-ray machines they could give detailed views on the body's complex structures such as liver or brain. These machines were developed by physicists. New technologies like those developed by the space programme contributed to the development of machines such as MRI scanners. Their importance was that doctors could now look inside the body without doing exploratory surgery.

Drug Discoveries

Drug research has contributed more to the progress of medicine during the past century than any other scientific factor. This is an interdisciplinary field in which discoveries have been jointly made by chemists and doctors, for example the work of Ernest Chain, a chemist was crucial in the development of penicillin. It was the big chemical companies such as Bayer and Wellcome that were able to fund discoveries and become the big pharmaceutical companies of today. Nowadays discoveries in medicine are most likely to come from biochemists in biotech firms and molecular biologists.

A drug is a chemical that is effective and safe in treating a disease or its symptoms. The first drugs were chemicals isolated from herbs of known effectiveness, for instance the painkiller morphine from opium and the malarial drug quinine from cinchona bark.

Chance and serendipity played an important part in the discovery of many drugs. If an unusual strain of the penicillin mould had not found its way into Fleming's lab we might not have had penicillin. But 'luck favours the prepared mind' as Pasteur said. It is too easy to walk past open doors and not look to see what is inside. If Fleming had just washed out his contaminated bacterial culture and had not observed and written about the effect of the mould the drug would not have been created. Other drugs were noticed to have beneficial side effects. Minoxidil used to treat high blood pressure was found to cause hair growth and is now marketed instead for baldness. Recently Viagra started off as treatment for angina. It seemed that trials were not giving the hoped for results and it was decided to end the trial but surprisingly many men refused to give back their tablets and asked where they could obtain more! It was then that researchers paid heed to a rumoured side effect – that it increased the strength of erections and the blockbuster drug [and saviour of rhinos] Viagra was born!

Massive screening of natural herbs and products was undertaken by the large chemical companies. in 1939 soil microbiologist Selman Waksman started to screen soil microbes for activity against pathogenic bacteria. Over the years his group isolated and tested some 10,000 cultures, from which came 10 drugs. The most important was streptomycin for tuberculosis, for which he won the Nobel Prize. Antibiotics, immunosuppressants, anticancer substances, and over a hundred of the most important drugs were discovered but by 1970 very few new substances were being discovered this way. Nature is exhaustible.

Ehrlich likened a potent drug to a magic silver bullet. A bullet can work if aimed at the proper target. Biochemists identify many macromolecules that control strategic links in the body's biochemical pathways. Pharmacologists choose as drug targets those macromolecules whose mechanisms are susceptible to intervention by small chemical molecules. Drug therapy currently works on about 500 targets. About one-half of drug targets are receptors on cells. About a quarter of known drug targets are enzymes that facilitate crucial chemical reactions.

Examples of drugs that work on targets are beta blockers. **Sir James Black** discovered not one but two of the most valuable drugs ever found by this method of analytical pharmacology. Black suggested, a synthetic compound similar to adrenaline might act as a false key, binding onto so-called beta-receptor sites and thereby preventing adrenaline from entering. This would be a valuable treatment for heart disease as it would block the effects of adrenaline. He took his discovery to ICI and developed propranolol, which is used to treat high blood pressure, angina [pain from the heart], prevent heart attacks and migraines. It quickly became the world's best selling drug. Black then began to investigate the possibilities of developing a similar agent to block the effects of histamine on the stomach and thus reduce acid secretion. The result was cimetidine the first of a group of anti-ulcer drugs – H2 receptor blockers. Launched in 1975 under the brand name Tagamet, cimetidine rapidly outsold propranolol and became the biggest selling prescription drug of any kind in the world, with annual sales of around $1 billion. Surgery for stomach ulcers became a rarity as a result.

Genes can also be drug targets, although their numbers are rather small at present. The human genome has now been sequenced. Cancer occurs when there is a fault in the genome and growth of cells is unregulated. In the last few years cancer genes have been sequenced, for example the melanoma gene at Nottingham University. Many are hoping that this will lead to the production of drugs that will only target the abnormal gene and that chemotherapy used in cancer treatment will be more effective and have fewer side effects as a result. At present chemotherapy for cancer works by mainly attacking rapidly dividing cells or proteins commonly found on cells; so drugs attack normal cells leading to gut symptoms such as nausea and diarrhoea and hair loss. Some are even predicting that all cancers will be cured or kept under control in the near future.

Blood Transfusion and organ transplantation

In 1901 Karl Landsteiner documented the three human blood groups. A B and O. This was later used to determine the compatibility between human blood groups and blood transfusion became established. Just before World War 1 a way of stopping blood clotting using sodium citrate was discovered. This meant that a transfusion procedure no longer had to take place with the donor and the receiver in the same place at the same time. Blood could be taken and stored and blood banks were possible. The availability of blood transfusion undoubtedly saved many lives and made surgery much safer. Later in 1940, ways were found of fractionating blood so that 'blood products' could be used appropriately. E.g. the blood product cryoprecipitate could be used to treat haemophilia, immunoglobulin from blood plasma can be used to treat chicken pox in immunocompromised patients.

Rejection of transplanted organs occurs because of incompatibility between the donor and the recipient as in blood transfusions. A person's immune system recognises 'foreign tissue' and sets about to destroy it. The first successful transplant was performed in 1954 by Joseph Murray who transferred a kidney from one identical twin to another. It was successful because the twins shared the same genes and the new body did not reject the kidney. He followed this procedure in 1962 with the first successful transplantation of a kidney from a dead body to a living one. Using immunosuppressive drugs during surgery, Murray stopped the recipient from rejecting the new kidney. The first heart transplant came in 1967 and was performed by Christian Barnard in South Africa but the recipient died 18 days later. The success ratio of modern transplants can be attributed to careful matching of donors and cyclosporin, an immunosuppressant. Cyclosporin prevents rejection by weakening the immune system. The weakened immune system does not attack the 'foreign' kidney but patients are more susceptible to illness. By 1984 two-thirds of all heart transplant patients survived for five years or more.

Organs that can be transplanted include the heart, kidneys, liver, lungs, pancreas and intestine. Tissues include bones, tendons (both referred to as musculoskeletal grafts), cornea, skin, heart valves, and veins. Worldwide, kidneys are the most commonly transplanted organs, followed closely by the liver and then the heart. The cornea and musculoskeletal grafts are the most commonly transplanted tissues; these outnumber organ transplants by more than tenfold. Recently successful face transplant and partial limb transplants have been performed.

Stem cells could possibly be used in the future to grow a patient's own organs. Skin has already been grown from patients' stem cells and used for grafting. In Oct 2011 a trachea made from stem cells was transplanted. The use of a patient's stem cells to grow their organs would overcome the problem of rejection as the tissue would not be recognised as 'foreign' by the immune system and the patient would not need to take life long immune suppressing treatment. This would also overcome the lack of organs available.

As the rising success rate of transplants and modern immunosuppression make transplants more common, the need for more organs has become critical. The need is far greater than the supply. Organ donors may be living, or brain dead. Brain dead donor's organs are kept viable by ventilators or other mechanical mechanisms until they can be excised for transplantation. Traditionally organ donors have come from two groups: road accident victims and brain haemorrhage patients. The improvement of road safety and medical intervention mean fewer are dying. Around 8000 people in the UK need an organ transplant each year, but only 3000 transplants are carried out [27% of the population of the UK has signed up to being a donor]. In the UK, we don't know how frequently – or with what level of sensitivity – relatives are asked to consider donation. We do know that 45% of British families, when asked, refuse to let an organ be taken – even when the patient has signed the organ donor register. Spain has the highest rate of organ donation in the world. They have a system of **'presumed consent' [or 'opt out' system]** in which everybody is presumed to have given their permission for their organs to be used if they die if their wishes have not been recorded; this can still however be overruled by their family. The BMA wishes to bring in a similar system here. Spain also has efficient teams trained in counselling families in every hospital.

Ethical scenarios involving blood transfusions and transplants are common. Candidates are often asked to choose 'who should get the transplant'.

In Britain a patient's position on a waiting list for organs depends solely on length of time they have been waiting, the tissue match and size match and their medical need.

Decisions are made in a non judgemental way. It may be reasonable to take into account the likely long term success of the transplant however and an alcoholic who is still drinking will have a poorer long term outcome after a liver transplant because his new liver is likely to get damaged.

Developments in surgery

Developments in anaesthesia have made surgery much more humane and the development of machines such as the heart-lung by- pass machine means that even work on a major organ such the heart can be done by attaching a machine to the patient's circulation to carry out the work of the heart. Improvements in Intensive Care have meant that risky operations have a much better chance of success.

Laparoscopic surgery, developed in the last thirty years has meant that surgery is often not as debilitating as before. Twenty years ago, if a patient presented with signs of an 'acute abdomen' it was usually necessary to do a laparotomy. The abdomen would be cut open using a wide incision [cut] so the surgeon could see what was wrong. Nowadays better imaging using CT scans etc may make this unnecessary but if an exploratory look is necessary, a laparoscopy is done. A laparoscope is a small fibre optic instrument. Two small entries are made into the abdominal wall, one for the fibre optic part and another for a rod that contains instruments. By looking at a screen relaying the fibre optic pictures and using the other rod which can contain distance held cutting and sewing instruments a surgeon can diagnose and treat. Fairly major operations such as removing a gall bladder can be done using a laparoscope. Because the incisions made are small and there is less handling of abdominal contents recovery is much quicker.

Robotics is a field that is developing. It allows much more precise surgery than humans can achieve. The Da Vinci Robot is a large and expensive example. Smaller cheaper ones are in development. A surgeon looks at a screen and controls the arms of the robot by using hand held controllers in a set up very similar to a Playstation. In fact laparoscopic surgical ability and ability in robotic surgery has been shown to correspond with a surgeon's ability at Playstation and other games! At last an excuse for all those wasted hours!

Endoscopic examination of the gut/urinary tract/reproductive tracts similarly allows visualisation of the inside of organs and treatment by instruments that can be passed down the endoscope. Cameras can now be made as small as a tablet. It will be possible to swallow a 'capsule' which will be recovered from faeces at the other end and have good quality pictures!

Medicine in the future

People who try and look into a crystal ball and try and read what the future holds are always condemned to fail, so it is with trepidation that I write this section. Of course I don't really know. Many great discoveries are made by chance and without a clear idea of their potential. The space programme of the twentieth century was frequently condemned as an immoral waste of money but it led to technologies such as satellite communications and MRI [NMR] scanners.

Enormous strides in life expectancy have been made but there are some who feel that increases above an age of about 90 yrs are unlikely to happen because the body suffers from the effects of aging. Humans, like everything in the world, are susceptible to chemical reactions that cause aging. Cars have a limited life span because they are susceptible to rusting and their components degrade. Similarly our cells are susceptible to 'rusting'; oxidation by free radicals and other process which eventually cause our bodies to stop working and die. Death can occur from cancers which are genetic mutations in cells and these become more frequent as we age. Add in increasing obesity and rising levels of diabetes and some will argue that increases in life expectancy are bound to plateau. However others think we might be at the start of enormous improvements in not just life expectancy but a healthy old age.

Telomerase

Even in tissues, such as skin, cells cannot be replaced indefinitely. The DNA strands have protective caps called telomeres. After each division the telomeres shorten. In this way the cell is programmed to self destruct after a certain number of divisions when telomeres become too short. Organs such as the heart and muscle become weaker and our cognitive ability declines as we loose brain cells that cannot be replaced. Scientists have discovered an enzyme called telomerase which seems to arrest the shortening and even lengthens telomeres. When a Harvard team removed then replaced the enzyme telomerase in lab mice not only did they manage to slow the aging process but they actually managed to reverse aging and mice appeared to grow younger. However a word of warning – cancer cells produce telomerase; this is why they are able to keep multiplying. It could be that the use of telomerase and copying the cancer's cells quest for immortality may lead to the formation of more cancerous growths. Research in this field has only just begun.

Replacement with stem cells

Stem cells are undifferentiated cells that have the ability to form different types of cells. For example adult stem cells from the bone marrow can form many types of blood cells. Embryonic stem cells can differentiate into any types of cell and are therefore called pluripotent cells. They have the capability to form nerve cells or heart muscle cells; these cells cannot normally regenerate. For example people who damage the nerve cells in their spinal cord are usually paralysed below the level of their injury because the nerve cells cannot repair and brain damage after a stroke is permanent.

Pluripotent stem cells can differentiate into any type of cells and so may be used to repair or replace nerves or even organs. They, at present have to be taken from dead embryos and because of this many people have ethical objections. Recently however scientists have been able to regress cheek cells and make them into pluripotent stem cells. Not only does this evade the ethical problems but it can mean that it may be possible to use a persons own skin cells to grow a replacement organ and because it is formed from his own cells there is no possibility of organ rejection.

Organs have been produced by removing dead organs such as a heart then stripping it of heart cells using a detergent like substance leaving a collagen frame. Stem cells were then injected into the frame and they self differentiated into heart cells and multiplied. The hearts produced even started pumping, but were too weak to be used.

So far stem cells have been used to form new retinas and have been successfully used in retinal transplants. The Lancet [Nov 23 2011] reported that a patient in Sweden had received the worlds first trachea produced from stem cells. The patient had a cancer in his wind pipe [trachea]. An artificial trachea was created by using a glass model to produce an artificial scaffold. Then stem cells were inserted into the scaffold then the glass removed.

Replacement with machines - prosthetics

Parts of people, for example arms and legs have long been replaced by artificial limbs. These have been poor substitutes for the real thing. However limbs and parts of the body are being developed that mimic the body accurately and because human design is flawed may surpass human body parts. Surgeons have developed techniques to attach artificial limbs to nerves so that the brain can control them as if they were normal. The bionic man may soon arrive. Maybe one could design different organs for different activities with the ability to change them as one changes clothes.

Blade runner" Oscar Pistorius of South Africa crosses the finish line during men's 200m.

After monitoring his track performances and carrying out tests, scientists took the view that Pistorius enjoyed considerable advantages over athletes without prosthetic limbs. On the strength of these findings, on 14 January 2008 the IAAF ruled him ineligible for competitions against able bodied men

Old dead cells and 'junk'

As you get older old, poorly functioning cells accumulate. 'Extra cellular junk' such as atheroma [which causes furring up of arteries] and amyloid [which is a substance found in the brains of Alzheimer patients] accumulate. This 'junk' acts as impediments to the functioning of the body – e.g. arteries get blocked by atheroma. Normally white cells try to 'eat' atheroma to dispose of it but fail and die and become part of the atheroma. It may be possible in the future to programme 'super white cells' to be successful at phagocytosis (engulfing) of certain substances

Nano-technology could be developed to send enzymes/ molecules inside cells and alter structures within cells getting rid of old obsolete structures which impair cell function.

Cancer -DNA Mutations

Cancer is the second most common cause of death in this country. Drugs are being developed that only affect the mutation and so the only cells killed by the drug will be cancer cells, a silver bullet of the kind Ehrlich wished for. This way the effects of chemotherapy on normal cells will be minimal and have few side effects.

Tests will be developed which are sensitive tumour markers, which detect the abnormal genes of cancers long before a cancer normally becomes apparent. The immune system reacts to cancers almost immediately by recognising them as 'foreign' and different. At present we only pick up most cancers when they have started to produce symptoms and signs. By then they have been growing for 3-5 years. Developing a test which detects the immune response to these cancers will allow the early accurate detection and treatment of cancers and therefore enable a very high cure rate. The University of Nottingham has been responsible for developing the early lung CDT [cancer detection test] which picks up antibodies for lung cancer. Trials in the USA have been very promising and it is going to be piloted by the NHS.

There are enormously exciting possibilities in treatment and you, the doctors of the future may be using them and achieving and transforming medicine in a way we only dream of. However such treatments are bound to be expensive, holding and comforting a patient while they die is cheap. Trying to provide perpetual youth to an aging population is going to be extremely expensive and if these treatments become a reality health care expenditure will explode. Will everybody be able to afford everything? What are the implications for our crowded planet? There will be many ethical issues to be resolved.

Chapter 3

The NHS

'Alex has benefited from the world class surgical skill, prolonged medical deliberation and limitless compassionate nursing. I wouldn't know how to calculate the cost of the time and resources that have been spent on making him well, and it's not over yet. That the NHS provides all that without burdening the patient or their family with the anxiety of how to pay for it is one of today's great wonders. Anyone who doesn't think that it is worth protecting has no imagination or no heart.'

Tom Bickerby's whole hearted endorsement of the National Health Service while describing the care of his son is a common sentiment. The NHS frequently comes top in lists of things people are proud of about Britain. Nigel Lawson once famously said that *'the NHS is the nearest thing that the British have to a national religion.'* It has certainly been the case that any politician who seeks to tamper with it has done so at his or her peril. It is always one of the most important election issues *'Can the Tories be trusted with the NHS'* was a common theme in the last election. David Cameron has said *'Tony Blair summed up his priorities in 3 words –Education, education education; I can sum up mine in three letters – NHS'*

The Beveridge Report was a key part of the founding of Britain's

Welfare State. In this report, William Beveridge identified five 'giant evils': squalor, ignorance, want, idleness and disease. As a result of the report, a National Insurance Scheme was set up to try to protect people from these giants 'from the cradle to the grave.' The National Health Service Act was passed by **Bevan** in 1948 after World War 2. It took over all of the hospitals and made all doctors, except GPs, employees. The BMA (British Medical Association) was initially hostile but accepted it when doctors were allowed to keep their private patients and GPs became independent contractors. It was initially thought that once the NHS was formed and everybody became healthier health care costs would decrease. Unfortunately this was not so and health care spending was declared *'a bottomless pit'* by Enoch Powell a Health Secretary.

'Since its launch in 1948, the NHS has grown to become the world's largest publicly funded health service. It is also one of the most efficient, most egalitarian and most comprehensive.'- nhs.uk

The core principle of the NHS is that **good healthcare should be available to all, regardless of wealth.** The NHS is **'free at the point of use'**[1] (free to see a doctor, you pay in other ways-through taxes, national insurance) for around 65 million people (2010). Only certain prescriptions and certain optical and dental services are chargeable – [These are free in Wales and Scotland.]

The NHS is this country's biggest employer. World wide it is the fourth largest. Only the Chinese People's Liberation Army, the Wal-Mart supermarket chain and the Indian Railways directly employ more people. In 2008/9 it received a budget of **£100billion.**

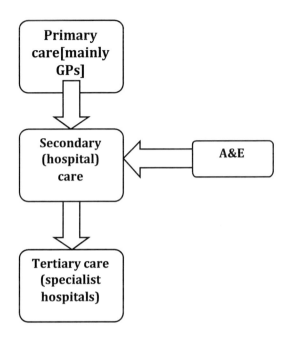

Structure Of The NHS

The Department of Health controls the NHS. The Secretary of State for Health delegates ministers to different areas.

Primary Care is the first point of call [excluding A and E] i.e. for medical services GPs. GPs are not employees of the NHS but 'independent contractors' - they have a contract to supply NHS services.

PCTs [Primary Care Trusts – soon to be abolished and taken over by **commissioning groups**] have the responsibility for GP services. They pay for GPs referrals. PCT s have to buy hospital services, they –'**commission** the service'

Until recently the only way you could be seen in hospital was by referral by your GP or as an accident or emergency via A and E. For this reason GPs are known as **'gate keepers'**. Their referral patterns have enormous cost implications for the NHS. They keep costs down for the NHS. In countries where people can self refer to specialists costs tend to be much higher. There are as many GPs as consultants and it has been calculated that 90% of the work of the NHS is done by Primary Care.

Secondary care is care by hospitals. GPs are not employees of the NHS but 'independent contractors' - they have a contract to supply NHS services.

Tertiary Care consists of specialist departments in Teaching Hospitals and specialist hospitals [such as Great Ormond Street Children Hospital]. These deal with relatively rare procedures and diseases .Patients are usually referred there by hospital consultants and GP s may not be able to refer them directly.

What is Governance?

Governance is the act of governing and managing. Good governance involves ensuring the safety, quality and appropriate spending of money in the NHS. How is this achieved?

1. All hospitals perform **'critical incident reporting'**. If a mistake has been made or nearly made it has to be reported and logged as a critical incident. It is discussed and measures have to be taken to ensure such a situation is avoided in future.

2. The Audit Cycle

Audit is the process of assessing, evaluating, and carrying out improvements to assess health care. Audit should be a 'cycle' because care is regularly reassessed.

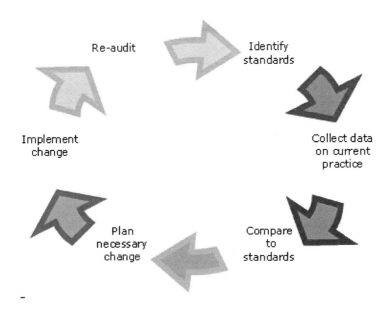

Re-audit

Identify standards

Implement change

Collect data on current practice

Plan necessary change

Compare to standards

'Whistleblowing' – Is supposed to be an obligation. Some hospitals have stated in contracts with employees that they are not allowed to inform third parties such as the press about any concerns they have. This is illegal and it is a duty of a doctor to ensure the safety of patients above all other considerations. A doctor can be struck off the GMC register if he fails to report concerns.

A Fairy Story to explain how the Health Care System works in the UK and USA

Once upon a time there lived a Gatekeeper and a Wizard in a green and pleasant land [the UK]. The Gatekeeper [GP] was very clever and his job was to see all the poorly people and cast magic to cure them. Sometimes the people were so poorly that the Gatekeeper had to open the gate to the Wizard's castle [the hospital]. The Wizard was also very clever and had a powerful crystal ball [scans] and special spells. The Wizard sometimes left his castle to go to the Ivory Tower where he was known as Professor.

Across the sea in another land a different set of rules applied. There were not many Gatekeepers and the people were able to go to Wizards directly. Although the Wizards were very clever at treating the really sick, it turned out that the Gatekeepers were better at telling who was really sick or not. And Gatekeepers charged much less for their magic. Nearly everybody who was seen by a Wizard got charged for his use of the crystal ball and the Wizards used far more potions than the Gatekeepers which were expensive and sometimes even harmed the patients. This led to very high costs and despite paying nearly three times more gold than in the other land, many people could not afford to go and see a Wizard or a Gatekeeper. The people cried 'This can't go on!' And a young Prince called Obama came who tried to change the system. As yet we do not know if everybody lived happily ever after.

Back in the old country the goblins were complaining that too much gold was being spent as many new expensive potions and spells were being discovered. They sent local inspectors to try to reduce the number of people the Gatekeepers sent to Wizards. The old Wizards were becoming anxious because Gatekeepers were being encouraged to use 'Any Willing Providers' rather than the traditional Wizards. The Gatekeepers were worried that they might become scapegoats for an underfunded and therefore failing system. This may let the corporate monsters enter the world. As yet, readers, we do not know how the story ends. We do not know if anyone lived happily ever after.

[Adapted from Mathers ,Hodgkin BMJ 1989 The Gatekeeper and the Wizard] and The Gatekeeper and the Wizard ,Redux. [BMJ 2009.doi] Douglas Kamerov and Liz Walton - A Jester joins The Gatekeeper and The Wizards [BJGP Dec 2011]

How does the NHS compare?

The NHS is funded entirely by the Government through taxation [except for a charge for prescriptions in England and Wales and some dental treatment].

France is said to have the world's best health care. French taxpayers fund a state insurer [Assurance Maladie] in proportion to their income, [the poor do not pay] and also pay co-payments which range from 30% to 70% of the costs. Ninety percent of the population also subscribe to supplemental private health care which usually covers the co-payments.

In Germany – All citizens have to have health insurance which individuals have to buy. The poor receive public help for their premiums.

The USA spends twice the amount of its GDP on health but has worse health care outcomes than virtually all developed nations. 58% of the population have insurance, some through work, but employers are not obliged to provide insurance. Medicaid and Medicare are government schemes which cover the elderly and the very poor. 15% of the population does not have any insurance and even if they do they often find exclusion clauses which mean that they are not covered. People with serious diseases are often excluded from health care policies unless they pay very large premiums. Inability to pay health care bills is by far the commonest cause of bankruptcy. President Obama is trying to bring in legislation to make Health Care Insurance compulsory and force insurance companies to take on high risk patients.

It is difficult to measure the efficiency of healthcare systems. In the UK life expectancy has been rising and infant mortality has been falling since the NHS was established. Both figures compare favourably with other nations. Surveys also show that patients are generally satisfied with the care they receive from the NHS. Importantly, people who have had recent direct experience of the NHS tend to report being more satisfied than people who have not.

Note that the UK spends less of its GDP on health than all developed countries. In a study published August 2011 based on figures from the World Health Organisation show the **NHS saves more lives for each pound spent than any other country apart from Ireland** over 25 years. Among the 17 developed countries considered, the United States healthcare system was among the least efficient and effective. [JRSM August 2011].

OECD (2007)   2

Country	Total health expenditure (per capita PPP US$)	Total health expenditure (% of GDP)
United States	7,290	16.0
Norway	4,763	8.9
Switzerland	4,417	10.8
Canada	3,895	10.1
Netherlands	3,837	9.8
Austria	3,763	10.1
France	3,601	11.0
Germany	3,588	10.4
Australia	3,357	8.9
United Kingdom	**2,992**	**8.4**
Spain	2,671	8.5
New Zealand	2,454	9.0

Problems with the NHS

Britain spends relatively little on health. This is reflected in relatively high waiting times and mid ranking cancer survival rates and survival rates for other diseases.

The NHS is a massive, centralised organisation and there is undoubtedly inefficiency in the system but it spends relatively little on management compared to other countries. Increasing efficiency may involve more 'bean counting' and increasing management costs– both of which are very unpopular.

It is an important institution to most people and high up on the political agenda therefore every Government feels obliged to 'do something about the NHS' to 'improve' it. There tend to be frequent massive reorganisations every time a new party gains power. Many doctors would argue the NHS is best depoliticised, like the Bank of England and placed in hands of someone like the Chief Medical Officer who would decide spending priorities.

All Health Care systems face potentially massive problems in the future. The **explosion** in **medical knowledge** and treatments combined with **aging populations** in developed nations means that some serious rationing decisions will have to be taken. It is unlikely that the NHS for example will be able to fund all new treatments. There is health inequality already between the rich and poor with the rich living on average eight years longer and enjoying better health throughout their lives. This difference will probably increase.

Health and Social Care Act

The Health and Social Care Bill has been debated at length and was passed in March 2012 but only after over 2,000 amendments had been made. The Bill will lead to increased privatisation and is committed to increasing competition in the belief that increasing competition and the number of organisations bidding for NHS work will drive down prices and lead to better services.

GPs in commissioning groups rather than PCTs [managers in Primary Care Trusts] will be responsible for deciding and awarding contracts to secondary care to provide services such as hospital care.

The BMA and most medical organisations have opposed the bill saying that it would lead to

. Reliance on market forces with an **emphasis on profit.**

- Unintended, knock-on impacts with longer-term consequences such an adverse impact on public health and medical education and training [the NHS currently trains and funds clinical medical students and junior doctors. Private companies providing care may not be similarly obliged.]

- Great potential for **conflicts of interest**. Patients may not trust their GPs to make appropriate referrals if their GPs were directly responsible for and financially benefited by decisions.

- The Royal College of GPs are concerned that **GPs** will be forced to **'ration'** services. The NHS has been ordered to make significant savings despite the fact that health care costs are increasing because of increasing medical knowledge and an aging population. GPs are worried that their responsibility for commissioning groups and controlling the funds will force them to ration services for which they will be **blamed.**

What is meant by 'privatisation'

This government, like the last is committed to increasing privatisation and competition within the NHS. **This does not mean that people will have to pay directly** for services [private health care]. It refers to the fact that **any organisation is allowed to set themselves up as a provider,** for example a company may provide counselling services and offer itself as an alternative to those provided by the local hospital. GP commissioning services will be obliged to look at and offer the contract to the organisation that provides the best value for money. This has been done for sometime for many services such as catering and cleaning in the NHS.

What is meant by 'cherry picking'?

There is concern that 'private providers' will **choose** ['cherry pick'] the most **profitable services** that attract most payment e.g. provide day surgery rather than care of the elderly or mentally ill.

Private providers have used exclusion criteria in some cases where they have excluded people above a certain age or the mentally ill or people who may need more and longer care – they 'cherry pick' the healthier patients. Because payments are set amount per procedure [called 'payment by results'] this would leave those more complicated and expensive cases for the NHS. It is important that when organisations bid for services that there is **'a level playing field'** i.e. the situation does not favour one group above another.

What is meant by Practice Based Commissioning?

GPs have formed commissioning groups and will be given control of funds to purchase services that they feel their patients need. For example they will have to purchase mental health services and, hip replacement operations, ultrasound scans. Patients will be allowed to choose between selected providers [e.g. which hospital they would like to go to.]

All procedures are given a set tariff [termed **payment**

by results] and because they have local knowledge and understanding it is thought that GPs are best placed to use funds carefully. In this country you can generally only access secondary care after being referred by your GP [except through A and E] because GPs make the referrals [see **Gatekeeper** role] This makes them the ideal people to ensure that services match the demands of the population that they serve. Because GPs have a new obligation to consider '**any willing provider**' of services the Government thinks that this new arrangement will encourage competition and better quality of care.

Disadvantages
- GPs will have to do **management work** which is something they have not been trained for and may not want to do [they wanted to be doctors not accountants didn't they?] This will **take them away from patient care** and they may **not** be **interested** or **good at it**.
- Although patients are offered a choice most do not really know where they want to go and ask their GP for suggestions or ask to go to their local hospital. The GP may have a **conflict of interest** e.g. they may do a session at a local hospital and refer them to specialist colleagues that they know. Or they may refer them to a minor surgery clinic that their Practice offers.

Public Health and The Public Health White Paper

What is Public Health?

Public Health promotes health and prevents disease in a population rather than on an individual basis e.g. vaccinating, controlling the spread of infections and legislating e.g. smoking bans. It is enormously important and cost effective. Most of the biggest jumps in life expectancy experienced in countries were because of simple public health measures such as sanitation. Life expectancy increased dramatically in the early 20th century and this was due to simple measures such as clean water and better nutrition. The effects due to the discovery of antibiotics and advances in medicine occurred in the latter half of the century and had a much more modest impact.

The prevalence of **infectious diseases has decreased** and Public Health has begun to put more emphasis on **chronic disease** such as cancer, heart disease and the prevention of obesity. Screening programmes – such as cervical smears, mammograms and faecal occult blood testing are part of Public Health. Public Health came entirely within the remit of the NHS.

What changes are being introduced in Public Health?

Planned changes in the white paper *Healthy Lives, Healthy People: Our Strategy for Public Health in England* states that;

Public Health will join with Environmental Health, under the control of Local Authorities and Local Authorities will have an obligation to consider the health of their population. This may be useful when it comes to planning applications. There have already been instances where a chip shop has been refused a licence to set up near a school. It may place an obligation on Local Authorities to consider more carefully the provision of parks and leisure centres.

However the Public Health Bill has caused most controversy with the plan to set up a public health committee consisting of officials, patient representatives such as Diabetes UK and representatives from the food industry, Pepsi and McDonalds are two companies on the Health Board and the idea that such companies have the power to decide on issues of public health is an anathema to many. The Government says it hopes to work with the food industry by **persuasion.**

This government has refused to take major public health measures such as the ban on trans-fats [a particularly harmful type of fat] or taxes on unhealthy foods, such as in Denmark. It initially refused to have a minimum price for alcohol [but seems to have changed and this may be introduced].The BMA was unhappy that it ditched compulsory traffic light labelling of food [to make it easier to tell what are healthy choices.] and the inclusion of representatives of companies such as Pepsi as important players in Public Health was seen as exasperating. However the government's slogan **'nudging not nannying'** sums up its policy of not dictating to people or industry but to try and persuade instead.

Social inequalities are an important issue in medicine and candidates are often asked question about them.

Question – 'What do you understand by inequalities in healthcare?'
Or 'How do social factors affect health?'

Inequalities in health exist when sections of a population do not have the same outcomes as others. It was thought that the formation of the NHS would lead to the elimination of inequalities. However they continue to exist. Edwin Chadwick published his "General Report on the Sanitary Conditions of the Labouring Population of Great Britain" in 1842. This showed that the average age at death in Liverpool at that time was 35 years for gentry and professionals but only 15 years for labourers, mechanics and servants. The Marmot Review recently identified that people living in the poorest areas die on average 7 years earlier than people living in richer areas and spend up to 17 more years living with poor health. The poor have higher rates of **mental illness**, and harm from **alcohol, drugs and smoking**, and **obesity**. They **consequently have higher rates of diabetes, heart disease and cancer. Cardiovascular disease [heart attacks and strokes] is the biggest killer with cancers as second in the UK**. These two are responsible for two thirds of all deaths; major risk factors for both are smoking and obesity.

Causes of inequalities

1. **Chicken and egg situation.** – Being ill means that you cannot work so hard and do less well in life and fall down the social scale. However being poor can mean that you also have poor health.

2. **The Inverse Care Law** - Those who are richer and better educated can access better facilities.

3. **The material explanation. [Being poor is associated with unhealthy habits.]** Poor housing conditions, poor education and less job satisfaction and higher risk occupations lead to poor health in the lower social classes. Poverty is bad for health. Diseases that afflict the developed world tend to be related to obesity and tobacco and alcoholism. Within the wealthy nations they are most prevalent in their poorest regions and the lower social classes.

If you were the Health Secretary what changes would you introduce to improve health and save lives and contain rising costs?

Remember Public Health is very good at improving the health of a population. In response to this common question it may be worth considering a scenario such as a tax on 'unhealthy foods.' but remember that could be seen as 'nannying' and may be difficult to implement – so have your arguments and ideas ready.

Primary Care is cheaper than hospital care so moving services out of hospital to GP practices and training GP s to have special interests for example in cardiology or dermatolgy and getting GPs to refer to them in the first instance might help keep costs down.

Providing respite care for the elderly or people who are recovering from operations who are not quite well enough to go home but not unwell enough to need an acute bed could also be cost effective.

What differences did you notice between the specialities you saw in your work experience?

General Medicine. [Medics or physicians]
A specialist has the satisfaction of in-depth knowledge of their speciality and being very good at it. They have the intellectual challenge of making unusual and rare diagnoses.

Surgery involved making a diagnosis and concerned with fixing it often that day so you almost got immediate results. Of course there were the lots of technical and practical skills involved with operating.

General Practice involved an enormous variety of patients of all ages and problems. Some problems were very minor, some serious and care of the patient involved knowledge and treatment of the patient **holistically. Continuity of care** is important and GPs generally get to know their patients better than hospital doctors and are able to review them a few days later if necessary which is hard to do with patients seen in a clinic.

Arguments for and against private healthcare

Justice [fairness] v Autonomy
Is it right that the richer should have better health care just because they have more money? Or should people have the right to spend their money on what they want [as with other things]? If people want to spend their money on their health rather than a sports car they should not they be allowed to?

Other arguments in favour;

It takes pressure off the NHS. Reduces NHS waiting lists

Some NHS hospitals make a lot of money from private patients, which goes back into funding NHS care.

It stops people seeking private care abroad

Against

Increases inequality.

Takes doctors away from treating NHS patients [the NHS has spent a lot of money training those doctors]

Private health care does not usually provide full coverage and patients after 'queue jumping' may have to be treated by the NHS

It is financially driven so doctors have a monetary incentive to do what the patient wants and carry out unnecessary investigations and operations.

Evidence Based Medicine/Treatment

Evidence-based treatment (EBT) is an approach that tries to decide the best treatments by identifying such evidence that there may be for a practice, and rating it according to how scientifically sound it may be. Its goal is to eliminate unsound or excessively risky practices in favour of those that have better outcomes.

EBT uses various methods (e.g. carefully summarizing research, putting out accessible research summaries, educating professionals in how to understand and apply research findings) to encourage, and in some instances to force, professionals and other decision-makers to pay more attention to evidence that can inform their decision-making. Where EBT is applied, it encourages professionals to use the best evidence possible.

The core activities at the root of evidence-based medicine can be identified as:

- a questioning approach to practice leading to scientific experimentation

- meticulous observation, enumeration, and analysis replacing anecdotal case description, recording and cataloguing the evidence for systematic retrieval.

Archie Cochrane was important in promoting evidence based medicine. He served as a doctor in World War 2 and wrote that he believed that much accepted medical practices had no evidence to justify their use.

He said, "I knew that there was no real evidence that anything we had to offer had any effect on tuberculosis and I was afraid that I shortened the lives of some of my friends by unnecessary intervention."

He promoted Randomised Control Trials [RCTs] of which the 'randomised double blind controlled trial' remains the gold standard way of proving the effectiveness of a treatment. In this patients are allocated at random to one treatment or another [possibly a placebo], it is double blind because neither the patient nor the doctor knows what treatment they are getting and so neither the patient nor the doctor's expectations can influence results.

He set up the Cochrane Library database of systematic reviews [Medline is another] which led to the establishment of the Cochrane Centre in Oxford and finally the International Cochrane Collaboration – which involves over 100 countries. Most advances in medicine now occur as the result of large randomised controlled trials on many patients who are enrolled from different hospitals and different countries.

Evidence based medicine has certainly improved medical practice. However the emergence of strict guidelines results in a disappearance of individual personal based treatment and the inability to dare to try unusual treatments.

NICE

The **National Institute for Health and Clinical Excellence** or **NICE** is an independent organisation set up to develop a series of national clinical guidelines to secure consistent, high quality, evidence based care for patients. NICE carries out assessments of the most appropriate treatment regimes for different diseases. These must take into account both desired medical outcomes (i.e. the best possible result for the patient) and also economic arguments regarding differing treatments.

NICE was established in an attempt to end the 'post code lottery'. In the past some PCTs would fund some treatments such as infertility while others would not. Whether you were eligible for treatment depended on where you lived. NICE has since acquired a high reputation internationally as a role model for the development of clinical guidelines.

A fast-track assessment system has been introduced to reach

decisions where there is most pressure for a conclusion for example when a new cancer treatment becomes available.

NICE uses the QALY [quality adjusted life year] to decide if certain very expensive treatments should be funded. If a treatment costs less than £20,000 for each extra year of good health it extends life by it will be funded.

The Multi- Disciplinary Team

Many different doctors from different specialities and professions come together to provide care for a patient. Candidates tend to over emphasise the role of doctors and underplay the role of other health care professionals. Other health professions include nurses, physiotherapists, occupational therapists [who assess patients and may suggest modifications to their home eg a walk in bath/stair lift] and social workers. For example a stroke patient is likely to have the input of doctors [radiologists and physicians], nurses, physiotherapists, occupational therapists, speech therapists [if the stroke affects their speech], psychologists who may assess their brain function and recommend certain memory aids etc and of course social workers who would be responsible for extra home care help or finding alternative accommodation such as a nursing home.

Always be appreciative of all these people **do not suggest that you think doctors are superior** in any way. Remember that your **interviewers** are **unlikely to be all doctors.** You may have a nurse or a research scientist. Remember that doctors are **not the only professionals** that **combine 'a love of science with its practical application** and with

working with people.' Others including physiotherapists and radiographers and today's degree holding nurses would rightly say that the description also fits their jobs.

1)http://www.nhs.uk/NHSEngland/thenhs/about/Pages/overview.aspx

Accessed 3rd July 2011

2) ^ OECD (November 2009). "OECD Health Data 2009 - Frequently Requested Data". Organisation for Economic Co-operation and Development. Retrieved 2010-02-05.
-

Chapter 4

Medical Ethics

Medical ethics; 'The standards of professional competence and conduct which the medical profession expects of its members.'

This is an important subject that comes up in virtually **all** medical interviews. More than anything interviewers want to know that the candidate is 'ethically sound' and has the **right attitudes** to become a doctor. This is the main purpose of the interview. You could be a genius but that is not enough to be a doctor. Often you are presented with an ethical scenario and asked to discuss it.

Most ethical problems can be seen as a **conflict** between the four main pillars of medical ethics [see below]

The four pillars of medical ethics

Most ethical scenarios in medicine can be discussed using the four principles of autonomy, beneficence [acting in the patient's best interest], non-maleficence [not harming] and justice.

		MEDICAL ETHICS		
A U T O N O M Y		B E N E F I C E N C E		N O N M A L I F I C E N C E		J U S T I C E

Autonomy

Autonomy describes the patient's right to **control over their life**. [Literally self rule]

A patient's autonomy includes the right to treatment, the choice of treatment and the right to refuse treatment. If a doctor does not obtain consent for a procedure the doctor can be charged with assault.

While a competent patient can always refuse treatments they cannot insist on a treatment that a doctor feels can cause harm or harm to others. A common example is when a patient comes into the surgery asking for antibiotics for what the doctor thinks is a cold. The doctor in this case should not prescribe them because there is no benefit, it puts the patient at risk of harm from side effects, and it causes harm to the population at large by increasing antibiotic resistance and creates an unnecessary expense which leaves less money for the rest of the population.

Informed consent.

In order to make the best decision about his or her future the patient must be fully informed about all possible treatments, their benefits and side effects. It is the doctor's duty to provide all the necessary information **in a way that is understandable.**

-Competence: a patient must be competent (or have capacity) to 'have autonomy.' This means that the patient is able to make his or her own rational decisions. Situations in which a patient may not have competence include: the patient having a mental illness or the patient being too young to understand the situation, having dementia or an emergency situation such as when unconscious or delirious.

Those suffering from mental illness e.g. mania or severe depression can be forcibly detained and forced to have treatment under the Mental Health Act.

The doctor can test competence through discussion: if the patient is fully able to comprehend the situation (not just repeat what the doctor says in parrot fashion) then they have competence. Usually competence is tested over a number of consultations as some patients may only be capable of competence on some days.

Consent for children to have medical treatment is usually given by their parents or legal guardian. The age at which they are said to be competent depends on their ability to understand the situation. [Fraser rules and Gillick competence – see later section.]

Beneficence

This states that the doctor should **always act in the patient's best interests** [which are not necessarily what the patient perceives as his best interests]. This includes providing the best treatment, searching for the best means and the best outcome.

In the past, this principle was overriding. Autonomy was extremely limited and the doctor was paternalistic [i.e. acted as a father to a child]. In some cases, such as in emergency, it is still overriding nowadays.

Non-maleficence:[Avoiding harm]

'Primum non nocere' (**first do no harm**)
This is often the first thing you will find in a medical ethics book. The principle of non-maleficence instructs the doctor to avoid doing harm to the patient. It demonstrates the understanding that medicine can potentially do more harm than good and that possible side effects and risks have to be considered carefully.

Iatrogenic illnesses or deaths are those due to an adverse effect or complication as a result of medical treatment. Iatrogenic illnesses include side effects. These can be, medical, or just anxiety or distress related to medical procedures. For example we may not consider someone waiting for results for a test on her baby for Down's Syndrome as suffering but the anxiety generated can be enormous and needs to be taken into account when thinking about screening procedures.
In a study carried out in the USA in 1981 more than one-

third of illnesses of patients in a university hospital were iatrogenic [caused by doctor's treatments], nearly one in ten of these were considered major, and, in 2% of the patients, the iatrogenic disorder ended in death. Iatrogenic illnesses are considered the 3rd most common cause of death in the USA after Cardiovascular Disease and Cancer. Medical safety issues are therefore of major importance; hospital and GP surgeries have regular 'critical event' analysis sessions where mistakes and near misses are discussed and measures taken to ensure that such incidents are avoided in future.

Justice

Justice is a difficult concept with a **number of meanings**. We will only deal with the two most common here:

1. Fairness

A doctor should ensure that there is justice [fairness] in the division of resources.[Distributive justice] All health systems have limits on the amount of money that can be spent. By spending enormous amounts of money on a single person [e.g.. Expensive cancer treatments that may have a small chance of extending a person's life by a few months] we are leaving less money to be spent on others. Is this fair? Is it fair to spend a lot of money on a liver transplant for an unrepentant alcoholic who is likely to damage his new liver? It might be in his best interest [beneficence] to have the operation but is it fair to expect society to pay for it?

NICE – The National Institute of Clinical Excellence was set up specifically to deal with **funding options**. As with any system financing health care, the NHS has a limited budget and a vast number of potential spending options. Choices must be made as to how this limited budget is spent.

2. Is it Against The Law?

Doctors, like everybody else have a duty to abide by the law. They are not for example able to flout the Abortion Act or carry out 'physician assisted suicide.'
[See example on request for help with suicide below]

Confidentiality

Although confidentiality is not one of the ethical pillars it is an important principle in medical ethics and was mentioned by Hippocrates.

'All that may come to my knowledge in the exercise of my profession or in daily commerce with men, which ought not to be spread abroad, I will keep secret and will never reveal'

It stops health professionals disclosing personal information and data without consent.
This is necessary in a relationship of **trust.** In order to be able to obtain a full picture of a patient's problems to enable diagnosis and treatment health care professionals need information. A patient would trust a doctor with information only if they were confident that their privacy would be protected.

Confidentiality **can be broken if** there is a possibility that not disclosing information could result in **serious harm to others**.

For example where a doctor suspects child abuse or if a patient has a serious infectious disease where not notifying patient contacts and treating them may put those contacts in danger. Gun shot wounds and knife crimes similarly have to be reported.

Non Judgemental

Always remember that **your opinions or beliefs should not affect your treatment of a patient**. All people including those with self inflicted injuries, drug addicts and even criminals should be treated with respect and beneficence. Your personal beliefs are irrelevant when discussing ethical scenarios.

The Abortion Act makes abortion legal up to **24 weeks** gestation,
1 If there is greater physical or mental risk or harm to the mother by continuing the pregnancy.

2. At any stage if there is serious risk to the health of the mother

3. At any stage the foetus is likely to be born with severe physical or mental abnormalities.

Pregnancy and delivery is more dangerous than a termination so reason number one suggests that provided the pregnancy has not gone far there is effectively abortion on demand. However late terminations, beyond 16 weeks are rare.

A doctor is **allowed to 'opt out'** of performing an abortion or referring for an abortion. However they must treat the patient and the patients view with respect and **refer her to another doctor willing** to help her. One must not forget that they may have distressed and frightened girl/women in front of them who is asking for help.

Always be careful **not to sound opinionated**. Advice to interviewers from one medical school includes the statement 'candidate should realise that **there is not necessarily a definite answer.'** A frequent pitfall that many applicants fall into is that they venture an opinion and then try to justify it too strongly when questioned. Do not be afraid of changing your mind if pressed, **flexibility is valued and stubbornness is not** It is likely that you will be pushed to arrive at a point of view but **always state** that **you would discuss any situation with colleagues, the hospital ethics board, the hospital's lawyers and your medical defence union.** In reality ethical scenarios involve a team of doctors and other professionals.

Children and Consent

Fraser Ruling and Gillick Competence

Mrs Gillick took her Health Authority to court because they were supplying contraceptives to under 16yr olds without informing parents. She had 5 daughters and felt that she had a right to know if they were being prescribed anything. The case went to the House of Lords [the then equivalent of the Supreme Court in the UK].

The judges, chaired by Lord Fraser, ruled that a child was competent and had autonomy and that their confidentiality was to be respected [i.e. their parents did not need to be informed] **if they fully understood the risks of treatment and its implications**. The doctor should try to **persuade the**

child to talk and share **information with its parents** but if the child insisted she did not want to, they did not need to be informed. In the case of contraception the doctor had to feel that there was a strong likelihood of sex occurring anyway and consider the possibility of sexual abuse [which should be always reported].

This case led to the term Fraser Rules and Gillick competence. A child is 'Gillick Competent' if he/she is mature enough to have understanding of what is involved – there is no arbitrary age limit.

These rules **apply to all medical procedures** not just contraception and abortions. A **'Gillick competent' child can give consent** to have a procedure against the wishes of her parents and has the **right to confidentiality**. However, a child is not able to refuse potentially life saving treatment if a doctor thought it was in their best interests and the parents also wished for it to be carried out.

Ethical Scenarios - Conflicts between principles

Conflicts with these principles create an ethical scenario. Almost all can be solved by considering these principles.

ASSISTED SUICIDE

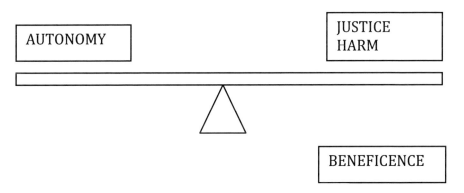

For example '**Assisted suicide**' can be seen as a **conflict** between a patient's **right to autonomy** – control over their life and the 'right' to end it if they wish and the doctor's duty to **do no harm** and the present **law** [which all doctors have to obey] which states that assisted suicide in this country is illegal.

On what side would beneficence go? Is a doctor acting in the patients best interests if they prolong a painful, unwanted life? The jury is quite literally out on this one and the issue is frequently in the news [see Debbie Purdy case below for current situation]

Assisted suicide is illegal in the UK but to date the law has always decided not to prosecute but to 'turn a blind eye'. It has been said that the law '**has a stern face but a kind heart.**'

However many have felt this to be cowardly

Lord Falconer said

''No one has the stomach to enforce the current law, because it is inhumane and further provides no protection for the vulnerable. The threat [of prosecution] forces some people to die alone and earlier than otherwise for fear of what may happen to those who accompany them''

Currently about two thirds of the UK population support Euthanasia in some form.

Slippery slope:

This term is not just used in medicine; it can be applied to many ethical issues. The argument states that a relatively safe, **small step can lead to a chain of related events which can result in a significant ethical change.**

For example: there is a slippery-slope argument against pre-natal genetic diagnosis for diseases during IVF (checking and selecting the embryos to avoid ones with 'undesirable genes'). It is difficult to determine which gene is an 'undesirable gene.' At the moment, we only use pre-implantation genetic diagnosis to check for serious genetic diseases that have been present in a family. Many people undergoing IVF have expressed a wish to choose the gender of their child-this is easily done but doctors ignore this request to try to prevent the slippery slope. If this was allowed, then why not choose embryos which are less likely to become obese or sickly? This could continue until we have **'designer babies'**: we would choose the colour of their eyes, how tall they are, how intelligent they are etc.

Although once on the slippery slope it is hard to stop falling, it is possible to draw a line somewhere. Some argue that a barrier can be erected to prevent further progression; this was evident in the Debbie Purdy Case and the current law on assisted suicide.

"SLIPPERY SLOPE"

Debbie Purdy, who has multiple sclerosis, wishes to end her life when she chooses. Presently because physician assisted suicide is illegal in the UK she would have to travel to Dignitas (a Swiss assisted dying organisation). She argued that if her husband would be prosecuted she would have to travel sooner rather than later i.e. while she was still capable of travelling alone because she did not wish him to face prosecution. She claimed that under The Human Rights Act she had the right to know under what circumstances her husband would be prosecuted. In September 2009, Keir Starmer, the Director of Public Prosecutions, announced guidelines on assisted suicide, indicating situations in which it is considered in the public interest to prosecute. In this way, Starmer created a 'barrier' by defining what is acceptable and what is not. If there was evidence of the following a prosecution would not be carried out;

- The victim had reached a voluntary, clear, settled and informed decision to commit suicide.

- The suspect was wholly motivated by compassion.

- The actions of the suspect, although sufficient to come within the definition of the crime, were of only minor encouragement or assistance.

- The suspect had sought to dissuade the victim from taking the course of action which resulted in his or her suicide.

- The actions of the suspect may be characterised as reluctant encouragement or assistance in the face of a determined wish on the part of the victim to commit suicide.

- The suspect reported the victim's suicide to the police and fully assisted them in their enquiries into the circumstances of the suicide or the attempt and his or her part in providing encouragement or assistance.

Example of an ethical scenario:

A middle aged man with inoperable cancer asks his doctor without any seeming emotion how he might quicken his death in the months ahead. He is still relatively well and is working and lives with his wife and daughter.

Answer:

Break it down into the medical principles

The principles of autonomy are weighed against those of harming the patient.

Physician assisted suicide is also against the law.

The doctor has a duty to obey the law but should approach the patient with sympathy.

Autonomy depends on the patient being competent – of ' sound mind' although he seemed 'emotionless' when he talked about suicide he may be depressed and may benefit from counselling or anti-depressants. Autonomy assumes that the patient is making an informed choice. The doctor will need to ask sensitively what fears the patient has and what is making him come to his decision.

A visit to the hospice and discussions about pain control may give him greater information about the situation he faces. He may not want to be a burden on his family but has he discussed the situation with them? Does he know what they truly want?

In summary the doctor should handle this situation with sensitivity allowing the patient to talk about his reasons and consider them carefully. It may be appropriate to discuss counselling and possibly anti-depressants. A referral to a hospice could help with his fears and the doctor or hospice can provide the expertise to reassure him about pain control and control of other symptoms he may develop. He should be advised to discuss his feelings with his family. The doctor and hospice could provide support to the family as a whole.

Example of an ethical scenario:

A ex- alcoholic patient, who is a mother of two children and a seven year girl both need a liver transplant. They have both been on a waiting list for the same amount of time. They are both likely to die without the transplant. There is only one liver. Who should have it?

A doctor must never be judgemental. Although a patient's illness may have been self inflicted, that is no reason to discriminate against a patient. There is also no reason to positively discriminate just because she is a mother. This issue should be decided purely by medical need and the likelihood of success of treatment and the length of time on the waiting list.. Ex-alcoholics may be in danger of relapse but the girl may have an illness that might affect her new liver in the same way. You do not know whose need is greater from the information given or who would be a better match for the liver.

You must also always say that you would make the decision after discussing with senior colleagues, hospital ethics committees or medical defence organisations etc.

Example of an ethical scenario

It is not fair that smokers should be allowed equal access to treatments if they refuse to try to give up smoking.

Remember the ethical pillars:

The statement 'not fair' refers to social justice. Why should valuable limited funds be used on such people?

However a patient's autonomy must be respected, a doctor should always act in the best interest of a patient and avoid harm. A doctor should act in a non judgemental manner.

There is a Slippery Slope aspect. If patients are refused treatment because of 'one self inflicted illness' then many other patients with problems such obesity and alcohol related illnesses could also be refused treatments. Where would it stop? People frequently take risks with their health. Would the NHS refuse to treat boxing or rugby injuries?

These arguments can be applied to any so called self inflicted condition. You could substitute the word 'obese' or 'alcoholic' for 'smokers'.

JUSTICE	AUTONOMY beneficence

Chapter 5

Important Organisations

The GMC

The **General Medical Council (GMC) registers** and **regulates** all doctors in Great Britain. All doctors have to be registered with it in order to work in Britain. It produces a Medical Register, a list of all people eligible to work as medical practitioners. It will ensure that all doctors undergo **revalidation and appraisal -** the process by which licensed doctors will demonstrate to the GMC that they are up to date. Revalidation was introduced after the GMC was criticised by the investigation into how **Harold Shipman** [a GP] murdered as many as 300 of his patients without anyone realising .He is thought to have been Britain's largest mass murderer.

It **handles complaints** about doctors about their 'fitness to practise' and has the power to revoke a doctor's license to practise [which results in the doctor being '**struck off'**] or restrict a doctor's work to certain areas only. The purpose of the GMC is to protect, promote and maintain the health and safety of the public by **ensuring proper standards**. It defines the principles and values which underpin good medical practice, to which all doctors practising in the UK must adhere.

The GMC also **decides the curriculum and sets the standards for medical schools**. It regulates and decides **post graduate training** in specialties and **appraisals** and **revalidation** for all doctors.

The duties of a doctor registered with the General Medical Council
[taken and adapted from the GMC Guidance to Doctors]

Patients must be able to trust doctors with their lives and health. To justify that trust you must show respect for human life and you must:

Make the care of your patient your first concern

Protect and promote the health of patients and the public

Provide a good standard of practice and care
Recognise and work within the limits of your competence
Work with colleagues in the ways that best serve patients' interest

Treat patients as individuals and respect their dignity
Treat patients politely and considerately
Respect patients' right to confidentiality

Work in partnership with patients

Listen to patients and respond to their concerns and preferences

Give patients the information they want or need in a way they can understand

Respect patients' right to reach decisions with you about their treatment and care

Support patients in caring for themselves to improve and maintain their health

Be honest and open and act with integrity

Act without delay if you have good reason to believe that you or a colleague may be putting patients at risk

Never discriminate unfairly against patients or colleagues

Never abuse your patients' trust in you or the public's trust in the profession.

The Royal Colleges

What do the Royal Colleges do?

The Royal Colleges such as the Royal College of General Practitioners, Royal College of Surgeons and Royal College of Physicians:

1.**Set standards for entry** to be a member via exams. You can practise as a specialist without being a member but most senior jobs are awarded to doctors who are members of the college of their speciality.

2.**Promote excellence in their speciality.** Each college publishes its journals and is involved in research.

3. **Lead and support doctors in the speciality.**

4.**Work with GMC** to provide advice regarding postgraduate training.

BMA

The BMA [British Medical Association]_is the professional medical association and **trade union** for doctors and medical students. It is the sole **negotiator for pay** and conditions with the Government as regards the NHS. This is particularly important because it is virtually impossible for doctors to go on strike. It **produces the BMJ** [British Medical Journal] a magazine for its members with research and topical articles. Not all doctors choose to be members of the BMA.

Chapter 6

Interview Formats

MMIs – Mini Multiple Interviews

A mini medical interview format is one in which there are a number of different stations in a timed circuit. The candidate is presented with a question or scenario and is marked on how well he/she performs. Studies have shown that the present UK systems of testing such as the UKCAT and interview scores are a poor predictor of how well candidates do during medical school. MMIs were designed and introduced by Mc Gill Medical School in Canada [also the first to pilot the PBL format] and have spread to many countries. Studies show that they can predict more accurately who the better students will be. They also eliminate interviewer bias because many different stations with a different assessor are used. The stations usually have a mark scheme so assessment is objective.

Currently a few medical schools use them at entrance at eighteen but many more plan to follow. Many more already use them at graduate level entry e.g. Kings. Medical schools have had 5-8 stations each about 5 minutes with 2 minutes between stations to look at the next question or scenario. Common themes in recent years have been;

1. Making mistakes, breaking bad n

You have been looking after your neig
she was on holiday and it escaped. O
over your neighbour's cat. Or a junio
a mistake that has resulted in the death of a patient and
as the senior doctor you have to break the news to the
patient's parents.

This tests your honesty and your sensitivity and soft skills,
for example appropriate body language, how you deal with
anger and distress. Actors and actresses are used and they
often shout, act angry and cry! One candidate I talked
to thought that they were doing really well until the actress
started crying [real tears] and sobbing! He described
feeling at a loss what to do next – he was not sure whether
to put an arm round her, comfort her or not and ended up
just standing in an uncomfortable silence!

2. Communication skills.

This tests your ability to listen and understand instructions
and your ability to give clear unambiguous instructions.
Challenges such as 'explain how you tie a shoe lace' or
describe this picture to me will test this. A picture may be a
scene in which case it is more important to focus on what
is happening rather than describe background information.
The picture may be a series of geometrical shapes which
you have to describe to another who will attempt to
reproduce it using your description.

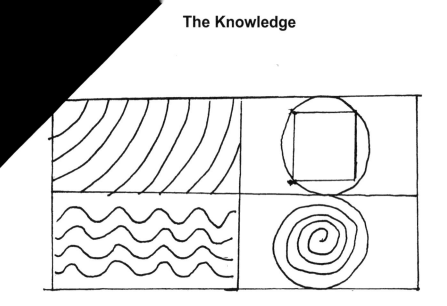

The above picture is on a piece of paper in a landscape direction and about 10cm x5. It is divided into 4 quadrants. In upper right hand quadrant is a circle with a square inside. The corners of the square touch the circumference; the circle touches 2 sides of the quadrant. In the upper left hand quadrant is a series of arcs of increasing diameter, about 0.5cm apart, with the upper left hand corner acting as the centre. In the bottom left hand quadrant is a series of wavy lines along the horizontal stopping about 2mm from the lateral edges and on average about 5 mm from the horizontal edges. The waves are about 5mm high [from trough to crest] and about 5mm apart. The bottom right hand quadrant has a spiral starting at the middle, going round in an anti-clockwise direction and touching the horizontal edges.

You may be asked to 'Describe this room to a blind person' – note it is important to establish whether the person has been blind from birth or recently and so will have a memory of colours etc.

3. Questions regarding the NHS

How it compares to other health systems, how are resources allocated, what challenges it faces, what changes are planned [obviously the chapter on the NHS, ,NICE etc. provides important knowledge.]

4. Your reasons for wanting to be a doctor

You may be asked a question related to this. For example why do you want to be a doctor not a nurse? Perhaps when answering you can say that you would like an in depth knowledge and medicine offers a more academic course. Nurses do an outstanding job but their work tends to be more protocol driven without the freedom to adjust to the patient's wider issues. Graduates particularly need to say what made them want to change career and perhaps describe a 'eureka' moment when they decided that they wanted to be a doctor

5. Questions relating to your Personal Statement

Again make sure you can talk about your extra curricular activities and your non academic achievements. Everything on your Personal Statement is fair game.

6. Questions relating to your work experience

Understand your patients thoroughly – make sure you know about their illnesses and that you can demonstrate empathy.

7. Questions relating to Medical History.

What do you consider to be the most important advances in health care in the last 200 years or100 years or 50 years or 10 years?

8. Ethical scenarios

You may be given an ethical scenario to discuss or to act out with an actor pretending to be a patient or a relative.
For example you may be given something similar to the following;

Dr X prescribes homeopathic treatments to his patients with minor self limiting illnesses. He does not believe that homeopathic treatments work but he says that his patients expect something so he gives them something harmless that may act as a placebo – discuss.
[use the Four Pillars to guide you]

Beneficience – Dr X thinks he is acting in his patients' best interest. The patient expects some treatment so he gives them something and because the patient trusts him the medication is likely to have a strong placebo effect and the patient may get better sooner than without treatment.

Non maleficence- Homeopathic treatments are so diluted that no harm can come to the patient while treatment with an antibiotic may give them side effects. Dr X thus avoids harming them.

Justice – Dr X is prescribing homeopathic treatments and spending public money on a treatment he considers useless, no better than placebo. This is a waste of public money. Treating the patient for minor illnesses will encourage that patient to think that he needs to be seen and prescribed medication if a similar illness occurs in the future. If Dr X did not prescribe anything but educated the patient about self managing such illnesses, consultations would not be taken up by patients who do not really need to see a doctor and resources would not be wasted in this way.

Autonomy. – Dr X is not respecting the patient's autonomy and right to make an informed decision. He is not explaining to the patient that he believes that the patient has a minor illness that will get better by itself. He is being paternalistic in his attitude.

9.Questions involving prioritising

In some MMIs an attempt is made to assess how well a candidate can prioritise. Questions such as;

'**You are 5 minutes away from a nuclear holocaust and you have to decide which ten people you should take with you in a nuclear bunker.**'

Here survival of the 'human race' is in question so it is important to take people who will help with that;

Fit, healthy [including mental health] intelligent adults. However older people have experience and the young can ensure continuity.

Equal numbers of men and women? One candidate quite rightly pointed out that one man can impregnate all the women so maybe you don't need an equal ratio – **It is your thought processes the examiners will be looking at.**

Skills – it would be important to have a farmer, builder and doctor [a GP perhaps better than a specialist], an engineer etc. Bankers, accountants and lawyers might not be so useful! Do you include a politician – leaders could be useful – it is debateable.

'You are going on holiday and need to pack. What five questions would you like to ask about the holiday and then what would you pack.'

You would need to ask questions about climate, is the holiday in a city or a jungle, what activities are planned? Are there any cultural requirements that need to be respected etc.

10. Questions about why you applied to that particular medical school.

You need to know about the type of course [PBL/traditional] and have read up about the University and the structure of the course.

Time management is extremely important. Many candidates have difficulty with this. The bell rings and they are still reeling from the shock of being shouted at in the last scenario but have only two minutes to think and formulate how they are going to present the next one. If you have an interview at a University that uses MMIs – **PRACTICE THE TIMINGS** so you get comfortable with knowing how to **pace** yourself those few minutes between stations are useful to plan what you are going to do. Listen to and look carefully at your interviewer who will often **provide prompts and cues to direct you.** These may guide you to specific issues that are mentioned in the mark scheme. It is a good idea to have a watch.

Oxbridge Interviews

The interviews at Oxford and Cambridge usually have the format of two separate interviews at two different colleges on two different days. You will usually stay a night in between the two interviews. Often one interview is quite personal and similar to the format of other medical schools with similar questions such as those based on your personal statement. The second interview may be more science based with **a greater emphasis on science compared to the normal interview format and academic skills.** Often questions are based on something you should know but you are then pushed to develop your thinking further. They are testing your ability to think laterally. Visit the colleges and talk to students there. You may pick up tips.

You may be given a task to prepare. You usually spend a night between your interviews and may be given a question such as;

'You have been given a hundred million pounds for research which field of medicine do you think the money would be best spent on?'

You will need to use your knowledge of health problems and the science behind them. Be prepared to be questioned on the actual molecular processes that may be involved in the disease.

Questions on graphs are common: For example you may be given a graph of life expectancy over the last two hundred years and may be asked to suggest and explain reasons why it is shaped the way it is. Your knowledge of medical history is important. Big increases were seen around the turn of 20th century because of better sanitation vaccination and public health measures, Female life expectancy increased particularly in the 1920s and 30s because of safer childbirth. The formation of the NHS had a more significant impact on women because they were unlikely to have been covered by work place insurance schemes. Antibiotics were an important advance etc

You may be asked to draw a graph of infection rates or predict epidemics of certain diseases. Questions you should ask include: Is it seasonal [spreads more easily in cold weather– eg flu virus], does it mutate easily or does infection lead to life long protection. E.g. some epidemics occur once every 20 or so years – once every generation so you should draw a normal distribution graph peaking every 20 years. Others such as the flu virus mutate very easily to form new strains and tends to be seasonal. How is it spread; by water or by air? How would this affect your graph?

You may be asked to draw a graph of blood drug levels against time. The mode of administration will affect the graph. If taken in tablet form, is it absorbed in the stomach or further down the gut? If injected intravenously peak levels would be achieved almost instantaneously. Subcutaneous and intramuscular injections would lead to peak levels being obtained more slowly. What is the drugs half life, how quickly is it metabolised?

Other questions that have been asked are similar to those mentioned in the MMI section on prioritising e.g. there is an epidemic and there is only one injection. Who should have it, you or me? Think about susceptibility and likelihood of increased severity of the illness. At present people with chronic illnesses such as cardiac disease, those with lowered immunity including pregnant women, those who are carers [look after the vulnerable or ill] including health care professionals are entitled to vaccinations such as flu before others.

Science questions are common –for example using your knowledge of the oxygen dissociation curve of haemoglobin and altitude. How would you weigh part of your body without cutting it off- such as your head or arm? Do mitochondria represent the ultimate in symbiosis? Is it really possible for James Bond to breathe while hiding underwater through a hollow thin reed? It is advisable to read your biology notes, particularly on human biology before the interview.

Oxford courses tend to be quite traditional, lecture based with little patient contact in the pre clinical years. You must make it clear how you feel this suit you. Advantages include the tutor system with small group teaching by your tutor.

Graduate interviews

Graduate interviews are often very similar but important differences exist;

You will be expected to **be more knowledgeable** about all the subjects discussed in the book and show greater maturity, insight and confidence than those applying straight from school.

You should be able to explain convincingly what made you change your career choice and drives your passion for medicine. Perhaps describe a **'eureka' moment**.

Explain how your first degree and other experiences can help you in becoming a better doctor.

The MMI format is more commonly used for graduate interviews than for school leaver interviews.

Overseas applicants

Candidates are often asked questions about the health care system in their own country and about their knowledge of the NHS. Questions about common diseases or health problems in their country of origin and social inequalities in health care are frequent. Again being able to compare and contrast with Britain is useful.

You may well be asked why you decided you wanted to come to this country, what attracts you to studying here? Living by your self in a different country in possibly a different culture can obviously be stressful. Questions about your support networks, any friends or family in this country, may be asked. You may need to draw on examples in your past that show your independence and resilience that demonstrate that you will be able to cope and make new friends.

Chapter 7

Which Medical School?

I am often asked which medical school is the **most prestigious.** In this country [unlike other degrees] it honestly **does not matter**. All medical degrees are valued equally. The GMC sets the curriculum and exam standards and 'external examiners' make sure that all medical student everywhere meet these. Nowadays when you apply for jobs through the deanery all applications are made anonymous, details like your age, sex, and **medical school** are **absent** from the application form. Only details like your exam marks, work experience, extra curricular activities and publications are deemed relevant and are present on the application form. And there is no such thing as an easy medical school to get into.

It used to be that local jobs would be linked to a local medical school so you would be best off looking for a medical school in an area you were interested in living and settling down in. Even this is not true now. You simply apply to the deanery who allocates jobs for that area and they will treat your application in exactly the same way as local graduates. I know of a graduate from Nottingham who got her first job at St George's Hospital Medical School London.

Your choice should be based on the **type of course** [systems based/PBL/Lecture based], the University and **the facilities** offered including **opportunities such as clubs and sports** and **the local area.**

.
Why this medical School? Is one of the commonest questions. You must do your research but the following points will help you.

System based courses

System based means that the course is divided into learning about the various systems such as cardiovascular system and subjects such as anatomy, physiology and biochemistry are integrated while teaching that system.

PBL or Traditional Teaching Methods

PBL – problem based learning

You are given a problem/scenario to resolve and normally work in small groups. Different members of the group will be allocated various tasks. PBL groups usually have a facilitator who ensures the group covers all the learning points and does not get side tracked.

Advantages of PBL

Practical view of medicine
Patient contact and their scenarios is what makes medicine more interesting
Requires active learning with students required to find

information for themselves
Small groups and team work
More interesting – facts more memorable if applied to a patient or scenario

Disadvantages of PBL

It is hard to cover everything you need to know with PBL at the end of the year there may be gaps in your knowledge
You may have to do extra work before exams to make up for your gaps
Requires a good facilitator
Requires a good team with each person doing their share of work diligently

Traditional Learning

Tends to be composed of two years pre clinical with basic subjects such as anatomy, biochemistry and pharmacology being taught. Clinical Medicine is taught in the final three years and patient contact is limited till then. It tends to be system based – you learn medicine by system – e.g. cardiovascular system or nervous system rather than using a problem which might encompass several systems at the same time.

Advantages of traditional teaching

Full information
All students receive the same information
Students have background knowledge before having to deal with clinical/patient cases therefore should have more understanding

Disadvantages of traditional learning

Sitting in endless lectures can be boring
Large lectures with hundreds of students means that asking questions is difficult
Patient contact may be delayed

Research your medical school – look up the Medical School website, Wikipedia. Attend the open day and talk to students studying there. They will be able to give you good tips.
 A few sample answers to; 'Why this Medical School?' follow. These are here to guide you but remember to make your answers personal. Why do YOU want to go there, how does it fit in with YOUR interests.

It is not possible because of lack of space to include tips on all the 32 Medical School but if you would like to contact me [details at the back of the book, information can be provided.]

Why Barts and The London [Queen Mary's]?

Queen Mary's School of Medicine formed when the Medical College of St Bartholomew's Hospital and The London Hospital Medical College merged in 1995. Both schools are steeped in history and are proud of their reputation for educating some of the world's most famous acclaimed doctors in the world. eg Parkinson who described Parkinson's disease a neurological disorder and John Hunter a famous surgeon.

Most of the teaching in the first two years takes place at Whitechapel, just behind the Royal London Hospital with the main Queen Mary campus situated in Mile End and St

Bart's Hospital in London. It is a cheaper part of London; accommodation does not cost as much as other areas and is very close to central London. The student accommodation is new and very nice and Queen Mary's is the only university in London to have a proper student campus with accommodation and facilities on site.

Students at Barts & The London will experience the hustle and bustle of London and will appreciate the wide range of patients they will encounter from studying in such a cosmopolitan and diverse city. Lots of immigrants therefore the chance to see diseases associated with immigrant populations such as TB, HIV. It covers many areas of deprivation [see inequalities section].

A massive £1 billion redevelopment project is currently underway in Barts & The London trust, with the rebuilding of the Royal London set to turn it into western Europe's biggest hospital when it opens at full capacity in 2015 – so an exciting time to be studying here.

Barts offers a problem-based learning (PBL) course, where basic lectures on topics and specialties are given and followed up by teaching on the wards in a patient-focussed manner. Students are expected to learn through curiosity, self-learning and motivation which can be a highly rewarding experience.

Rag week is awesome – always raises more money than other medical schools with lots of activities. Lots of student clubs – tell them what you are interested in.

The Knowledge

Glasgow interviews

Applicants will usually be interviewed by two people, the interview lasts about 15-20 min. They are reasonably informal. The interviewers are looking to assess;

1.Candidate's commitment to medicine.[work experience and reasons for wanting to be a doctor]

2 Evidence of hobbies and charity work

3. Evidence of team working

4. Key qualities necessary to be a doctor

5. Knowledge of Glasgow Medical School and the type of course. .

6. evidence of interest in medicine [current topical issues]

The Medical School is one of the largest and oldest in Europe. Numerous famous doctors studied at Glasgow including **Lister.** It is housed in a **beautiful modern building** and has **excellent facilities**. Glasgow is the biggest city in Scotland and has a **diverse population.** There are many immigrants and a lot of poverty and inequality. Glasgow has high rates of heart disease, diabetes and cancer [those diseases associated with poverty] - it is the home of the fabled deep fried Mars bar. It would be an interesting place to study and work in.

The course has a unique **spiral structure**. It is a systems based course using a lot of **PBL** but incorporating all methods of teaching including case based learning and lectures where more appropriate. Dissections of cadavers are one of the methods used to teach anatomy.   Clinical and non-clinical modules have been combined in the 'spiral structure' where core subjects are taught early on and as one progresses up the Medical School there is the opportunity to revisit topics adding more clinical focus and depth

Why Kings?

King's College Medical School is the largest medical school in Europe and has facilities to match. As well as excellent research facilities it has a wide range of sports clubs. These include hockey, football, rugby, cricket, tennis and netball. Rowing takes place on the river Thames by Chiswick Bridge, 800m from the University of London boathouse. The Strand has a rifle range and Guy's Campus has a swimming pool and gym and many music, singing and dancing clubs. '**I am very keen on contributing to student life** and would like to join --------------- club.' is always a useful phrase to use.

There are many excellent libraries and the Hodgkin Library at Guys Campus is open twenty four hours a day

As well as other medics you will be able to meet a diverse group of students from many other countries studying many subjects – the humanities and arts as well as sciences.

It is located in the heart of London – just under the new Shard, the tallest building in the UK. London is a varied, vibrant city with many museums, galleries and shows to enjoy. There is a diverse population with **lots of inequalities in health**, with wealthy areas along the river but with a lot of poverty around the teaching hospitals. The high immigrant population means that you will be able to see many diseases such as sickle cell [Kings has the leading sickle cell unit in Europe] and TB. Having three campus sites increases this variety.

It uses mainly lecture base teaching with a strong emphasis on anatomy dissection and little PBL. PBL can be hit and miss with some PBL groups and facilitators being better than others. PBL often does not cover the whole syllabus and can leave gaps in knowledge. Students do get the opportunity to see patients with first years making GP visits within the first couple of months so although learning is traditional your interest in patients and their stories is also catered for.

It repeatedly features as one of the top 25 universities in the World (QS World Rankings) having placed 21st in 2010. Kings has had a proud record of 10 Nobel Laureates in the staff and alumni of King's who made major contributions to 19th-century science, medicine and public life in general. They include: James Maxwell, one of the world's greatest physicists

- Florence Nightingale (1820-1910) founded the world's first professional school of nursing at St Thomas' Hospital in 1860

- Joseph Lister, Professor of Clinical Surgery at Kings from 1877 to 1893, introduced an antiseptic system which changed the practice of medicine and drastically reduced mortality rates from major operations.

Maurice Wilkins and Rosalind Franklin at Kings, made crucial contributions to the discovery of DNA's structure in 1953, which Watson and Crick found invaluable. In their honour, today KCL has the Franklin-Wilkins building, the main part of the Waterloo Campus

Why Liverpool?

The campus is just half mile away from the city centre, so very accessible. Liverpool is a lively, friendly and inexpensive city in which to live, work and study. It was awarded the accolade European City of Culture in 2008.

Liverpool medical school was the first in the UK to adopt a PBL approach to the curriculum and this is now well established into the modern, integrated medicine programme.

£72m is being invested in state of the art facilities for research in the Old Liverpool Royal Infirmary, including the establishment of a Centre for Personalised Medicines.

Applicants are invited to a 15 minute, semi-structured interview with two people, including academic members of the University staff, doctors and members of Local NHS trusts. The criteria used to assess the interview are: application of knowledge of the Liverpool medical programme and its curriculum, medical ethics and team work, together with the non-academic criteria. Each interviewer independently scores the candidate in each of these areas.

Why Manchester?

Manchester is a well known and respected University and one of the largest in Europe, famous for its teaching, research and academic record. The University is modern and dynamic with a culturally and ethnically diverse student population. This makes it possible to meet lots of different people from different countries and its size means that there are many clubs. *[Which clubs would you like to join – look them up]* The city of Manchester is student friendly and guarantees accommodation to all first year students. It has the advantages of a big city but is more compact and cheaper than London.

Manchester medical school uses the PBL method of learning. Students have an academic and clinical advisor who mentors the student from year one till graduation. There is clinical hospital and community based experience throughout the programme. It has excellent anatomy facilities, offering whole body dissection and a dedicated team of teaching fellows in anatomy alongside traditional lecturers and professors, to deliver anatomy teaching. There are also opportunities to specialise and do an intercalated degree.

You can also study in Europe [the Erasmus scheme] – if you have a language skill.

The interview; This starts with a half hour group discussion usually on an ethical scenario. Remember they are looking for a well reasoned discussion rather than a 'right answer'.

It is then followed by three stations – They may examine your reasons for choosing medicine, your charity/community work/ work experience. One may be about your knowledge – about the NHS and topical issues.

Why UCL?

UCL is ranked 7th in the world's top 10 universities [2010] and the medical school is ranked the best in London.

The Medical School is associated with famous teaching hospitals such as Great Ormond Street and Moorefield's Eye Hospital.

It has an inspiring history. It was set up by Bentham in the 1800s [UCL still has his preserved head and skeleton – which is often stolen by opposing Medical Schools in Rag week] Bentham was a famous utilitarian [utilitarianism is the belief in the greatest good for the greatest number of people]. UCL was set up to open up and make education available to people, **including women** from all backgrounds, not just the privileged and to people of all faiths. Bentham's secretary was Edwin Chadwick who is known as the 'father of the sanitary idea'. He had a major impact on the improvement of the population's health and life expectancy. He diligently provided evidence that showed that poor health and mortality were linked to sewage and dirty water. His work led to the Public Health Act.

Other inspiring people include Alexander Bell, Frances Crick [Watson and Crick discovered the structure of DNA] and Sir James Black [discovered beta blockers and H2 antagonists].

UCL has a large number of foreign students [30%] and is situated in London a large multi-cultural city –There is always a lot to do in London; concerts, theatres and galleries. The patient population is hugely diverse, multi-ethnic with diseases such as TB, HIV prevalent, as well the usual western health problems. There are **lots of health inequalities** and patients will include the very poor and homeless as well as the very wealthy.

The **Course is not PBL**

Chapter 8

Commonly Confused Terms

The following terms often seem a source of confusion. Candidates answer questions about them poorly so I have included and explained them in this section.

What is rationing?

Cost containment is important in any health care system; money should not be spent unnecessarily. Rationing extends further to limiting treatments that benefit patients. This should not happen and most governments will deny that they do this. However NICE will not recommend treatments unless they have been shown to improve outcomes for patients and some expensive types of chemotherapy are not funded by the NHS because of their cost and the fact that they only increase life expectancy by a few months. Organ transplants are rationed because of the scarcity of donor organs.

Many regard rationing as inevitable. With increasing medical technology and an aging population health care costs are going to grow however the Government is committed to reducing the NHS budget. One of the main objections of GPs to the Health and Social Care Act is that GPs on commissioning groups will be forced to extend rationing. The power and responsibility for the Health Service has been likened to 'a poisoned chalice.'

and GPs are concerned that the doctor- patient relationship will be harmed if they no longer simply act as the patient's advocate but have other agendas such as rationing care to meet budgets.

What is meant by complementary medicine/alternative medicine?

Alternative and complementary medicine both describe any treatment that is not part of conventional medicine. It is usually based on historical or cultural practices rather than scientific evidence. E.g. Reflexology and homeopathy. The NHS rarely funds such treatments.

Most types of complementary medicine have **no evidence** base but a few such as acupuncture have been accepted as being better than placebo for limited conditions such as back pain. It is thought that patients generally feel better because practitioners tend to spend a lot of time with the patient and develop **a therapeutic relationship**. 'The doctor as the drug' is a well known part of the doctor patient relationship and placebos are known to work. If the patient expects to get better they often will even if they have been simply given a sugar pill.

Richard Dawkins the famous atheist and evolutionary biologist defined alternative medicine as "*a set of practices that cannot be tested, refuse to be tested or consistently fail tests.*" He says '*There is only medicine that works and medicine that does not work. If a technique is demonstrated effective in properly performed trials it ceases to be alternative and becomes mainstream.*'

In the past Cognitive Behavioural Therapy [counselling] was

considered alternative medicine but has now been accepted as mainstream and is used a lot in the NHS.

Various organisations such as 'Quackwatch' have been set up to protect a 'gullible public.' Eighteen months ago a pharmacy was reported to the Royal Pharmaceutical society for selling homeopathic anti-malarials because the treatment suggested that it would be an adequate substitute for conventional anti-malarials. Despite the risk to life that these homeopathic tablets posed the complaint was not upheld.

Complementary/alternative treatments remain very popular with the general public with reports that about 40% of the public use them. Complementary suggests that they are used in addition to conventional medicine so that the likelihood of harm is limited because the patient is also seeing a conventional doctor. Alternative suggests that the patient is not seeing a conventional doctor and the potential for harm or delaying diagnoses is much higher.

Holistic Medicine

Holistic medicine means **considering the complete person** with all their illnesses, and their **mental, social and spiritual** well being. It looks for underlying causes for example headaches and depression may be due to domestic abuse.

It is a **common misconception** that holistic medicine is just complementary medicine. Many complementary practitioners do have long appointments with patients and spend a long time getting to know them and empathising with them. Doctors some times get into bad habits of thinking about patients in terms of their diseases eg the diabetic in bed 3 or the fractured femur in bed 4 **however holistic medicine should be practised by all doctors** especially GPs who are responsible for the patient as a whole.

What is vivisection?

Vivisection means surgery carried out on live animals for experimental reasons. This is rarely performed nowadays. All experiments or trials have to be agreed by ethics committees. If there is no other way of carrying out a trial other than by live dissection anaesthetics are given.

Animal testing in general also remains controversial. If asked about it, it is reasonable to say that where ever possible, alternatives should be considered e.g. testing on cell cultures. If that is not possible experiments should be carried out as humanely as possible and the necessity of the experiment carefully considered. However in some cases, such as the testing of effective pain killers, inflicting pain may be necessary and preferable to testing on humans.

Chapter 9

The Night/Morning Before The Interview

Read your Personal Statement and refresh your knowledge of what you wrote.

Go over examples of work experience.

Go over examples of charity work and extra curricular activities. What have you learnt from them and how would it make you a better doctor?

Look at newspaper articles for health related stories. Useful websites include: BBC health, patient.co.uk

At the interview remember nerves are normal - most actors and athletes say they perform better because of them. Feeling nervous or excited is physiologically the same. Reframe those nerves as excitement. If you come across as enthusiastic that is a major plus!

And remember - you are well prepared. You have a good chance of becoming part of the most exciting and looked up to profession in the world. You CAN do well at your interview!

Good Luck!

'Luck favours the prepared mind'

'Louis Pasteur'

Appendix A

The Career Path

5 years at Medical School minimum
+1 if you do an intercalated BSc [This is compulsory in some Medical Schools]

↓

Foundation year 1

↓

Foundation year 2

↓

Basic medical Training/Basic surgical training/   GP vocational training
2 years

                                                        2 years of hospital jobs

↓   ↓

                                               +1 year as a GP registrar

Higher speciality training   ↓

                                       GP [aprox 5 years in total]

3 years
↓

1-3 years sub speciality training

↓

Consultant
[aprox 10 years in total]

Appendix B

COMMONLY ASKED QUESTIONS

Work experience

1. Tell me about your work experience.
   (see pages 6 - 12)

2. Tell me about an interesting patient you saw during your work experience.
   (see pages 6 - 12)

3. What did you learn from your work experience?
   (see pages 6 - 12)

4. How did the roles of doctors differ in General Practice and hospital medicine?
   (see pages 68,118,119)

5. Did you notice any difference in the way different doctors worked?
   (see page 68)

6. How important was team work when you did your work experience?
   (see page 72)

7. What did you enjoy most and least about your work experience?
(see pages 6 - 12, 72)

8. Did you come across any ethical dilemmas during your work experience?
(chapter 4)

9. What type of doctor would you like to become?
(see page 68)

10. Where do you see yourself in 10 years time?
(see page 68, appendix A)

<u>Why Medicine?</u>

11. What have you done to make sure medicine is the right course for you?
(pages 6 - 12 on work experience may help. Chapters 2 and 3 may help that you are well read and informed)

12. Why do you want to be a doctor?
(see pages 8 and 9)

13. Why a doctor and not a nurse or physiotherapist?
(see page 9)

14. Why do you want to be a doctor and not a paramedic?
(see pages 8 and 9)

15. Why do you want to be a doctor and not an engineer? Don't you think that engineers have a love of science and help people?
(see pages 8 and 9)

16. How would you dissuade someone from doing medicine? Can you think of any drawbacks to being a doctor? (see page 8)

17. What are you most looking forward to and least looking forward to in a career in medicine? (see pages 8 and 9)

18. How would you cope with a death of a young patient in your care? (remember a doctor should have empathy but there should always be a professional distance between patients. Otherwise judgement could be clouded. It is against GMC guidance to treat your own family members or friends. Pages 17 and 18 on dealing with stress could help with answering this question)

19. Do you know how long it takes to be a consultant or GP? (see Appendix A)

20. What other roles do doctors have apart from treating patients? (see Chapter 3, roles include educating and teaching students, juniors and others especially patients; research, audit and management tasks such as commissioning; GPs run their own practice which is a small business.)

Personal insight

21. Tell me about your hobbies. (see page 13)
22. Tell me about your charity work.

(see page 12)

23. Do you have any weaknesses or strengths?
(see pages 14 - 17)

24. What would you like to most change about yourself and why?
(see pages 14 - 17)

25. Tell me about a time when you made a mistake. (see pages.
(see pages 14 - 17)

26. Do doctors make mistakes?
(see page 16)

27. Tell me about a time when your communication skills made a difference.
(see pages 14 and 15)

28. Tell us about a time when you were involved as part of a team. What did you learn from it?
(see pages 12 and 13)

29. Are you a leader or a follower?
(see pages 14,18 and 19)

30. Do teams need leaders?
(see pages 14 and 15)

31. What are the advantages of working in a team? What are the disadvantages?
(see pages 14 and 15)
32. How do you handle conflict in a team?

(see pages 14 and 15)

33. Which people are in the multidisciplinary team?
    (see page 72)

34. Tell us about your leadership skills.
    (see pages 14 - 19)

35. How would your friends describe you? How would your enemies describe you?
    (see pages 16 - 18)

36. How would you like to be remembered?
    (see pages 16 - 18)

37. How do you cope with criticism?
    (see pages 16 - 18)

38. How would you cope with stress?
    (see pages 17 - 18)

39. What do you do to relax?
    (see pages 17 - 18)

40. What is empathy?
    (see page 18)

41. Is it right for doctors to feel for their patients?
    (see page 18)

42. Is medicine a science or an art?
    (see pages 18 and 19)
43. Do you prefer working by yourself or as part of a team?

(see pages 18 and 19)

44. Tell me about an important person who you admire.
    (perhaps someone from Chapter 2?)

45. What are the positive aspects and negative aspects about a career in medicine?
    (see pages 8 and 9)

Testing Knowledge and interest

46. Tell me about Hippocrates.
    (see page 23)

47. What do you consider to be the most important advances in medicine in the last 200 years/100 years/ 50 years/20 years?
    (see chapter 2)

48. Can you tell me something about the history of medicine that interests you?
    (see chapter 2)

49. What do you consider to be the most exciting field in medicine at the moment and why?
    (see pages 45 - 50)

50. What do you consider to have been the most important medical discovery in the last 200 yrs/100 yrs/50 years?
    (see chapter 2)

51. If you were given £50 million to spend on research how

would you spend it?
(see pages 45 - 50)

52. Tell me about a recent advance in medicine.
   (see pages 45 - 50)

53. Do you read any journals? Tell us about a few interesting articles.
   (It is a good idea to read a journal before the interview and summarise a couple of articles)

54. Tell me about something you have read or a film or programme you have seen.
   (Again have a few ideas. It does not have to be medically related)

55. What does public health mean?
   (page 64)

56. Do you know of any changes in public health?
   (pages 64 and 65)

57. What do you think was the most important public health advance in the last century
   (page 64)

58. What do you think of doctors who smoke? Should doctors be expected to set an example to their patients?

59. If you were the health minister what changes would you introduce to save money?
   (page 67)

60. What do inequalities in health mean?

(pages 66 and 67)

61. How do you think social class affects health and why does it affect health in this way?
(pages 66 and 67)

62. Tell me – what are the main principles of the NHS?
(pages 51 and 52)

63. What changes is the Health and Social Care Act bringing to the NHS.
(pages 60 - 63)

64. What is GP commissioning?
(pages 62 and 63)

65. What are the advantages and disadvantages of making GPs in charge of commissioning hospital services?
(pages 62 and 63)

66. What is meant by the privatisation of the NHS?
(page 61)

67. How is the NHS funded?
(pages 51 and 52)

68. How does the NHS compare with health care systems in other countries? What kind of health care systems are there in the world?
(pages 56 - 58)

69. Is the NHS efficient?
(pages 56 - 58)

70. Where is most of the work in the NHS done, in primary care or secondary care?
(page 54)

71. What is meant by primary care?
(pages 53 and 54)

72. What problems does the NHS face?
(pages 59 and 60)

73. Who is the Minister for Health?
(Currently Andrew Lansley but likely to change soon)

74. Have you read about any health related topics recently?
(chapters 2 and 3 could help you answer this)

75. Was it a waste of money to send people to the moon? Surely that money would have been better spent on saving lives?
(pages 37 and 45)

76. Have you heard of the audit cycle?
(page 55)

77. What is MRSA? Why is it a problem?
(page 36)

78. Is it unethical for people to receive better treatment just because they can afford private health care?
(pages 68 - 69)

79. Tell me about any health related subjects in the news.
(see facebook page for up to date information and discussions)

80. What is NICE?
    (page 71)

81. What is rationing. How does the NHS decide what to
    fund?
    (pages 116 - 117)

82. How are expensive drugs rationed?
    (page 71 and 116 - 117)

83. Have you heard of evidence based medicine?
    (pages 69 - 71)

84. What is meant by holistic medicine?
    (pages 118 - 119)

85. What does the GMC do?
    (pages 89 and 90)

86. Have you heard of Harold Shipman?
    (page 89)

87. Which organisation controls medical education? What do
    the Royal Colleges do?
    (pages 90 - 92)

88. What are the major causes of death in the UK?
    (page 78)

89. What would be the most cost effective way of saving
    lives?
    (page 64)

90. Tell me, what do you know about cancer?
    (page 49)

91. Cardiovascular disease is the commonest cause of death
    in this country. What are the risk factors for cardiovascular
    disease?
    (smoking, high blood pressure, diabetes, high lipid levels,
    a strong family history, obesity)

Ethics

92. A 14 year old girl comes to your surgery and requests
    contraception. How do you handle this scenario?
    (pages 81 and 82)

93. A 14 year old boy needs a blood transfusion. His parents
    are strict Jehovah's Witness Church members and refuse
    the transfusion. What do you do next?
    (pages 81 and 82)

94. Is it right for the NHS to fund plastic surgery?
    (page 71, Cosmetic surgery is only funded in exceptional
    circumstances e.g. if not having it leads to severe
    psychological harm. Plastic surgery includes treatments
    such as those for burns and skin cancers.)

95. Should smokers or the obese be allowed equal access
    to treatments when they seemingly refuse to do anything
    about improving their health themselves?
    (pages 89 and 90)

96. Should people who indulge in extreme sports and get
    injured expect the NHS to treat them for free?
    (pages 88 and 89)

97. Should alcoholics get liver transplants?
(pages 88 - 90)

98. What is euthanasia? Is it legal? Should it be legal?
(pages 83 - 86)

99. A terminally ill patient tells you that his pain is poorly controlled and he is a burden to his family and society and wishes to die. He asks you to help him, what would you do?
(pages 86 and 87)

100.   Animals that are suffering are put down; do you think humans should also be put down if suffering and unlikely to recover?
(pages 83 - 86)

101.   Your patient has just been diagnosed with HIV. You find out he has not told his wife. Should you break confidentiality and tell her?
(pages 79 - 80)

102.   A patient has been seriously assaulted in an attack by her partner. You fear for her safety but she refuses to report it to the police. Is there anything you can do? Can you break confidentiality?
(pages 79 - 80)

103.   Someone comes into casualty with a serious knife wound and asks you not to tell the police who are outside. What do you do?
(page 80)

104.   A 14 yr old girl wants an abortion. She is adamant that her parents are not to be told. What issues arise in this scenario?
(pages 81 and 82)

105   A child has a haematological disease which can be treated by a bone marrow transplant from a matching donor. Is it right for the parents to undergo IVF and embryo selection in order to have a baby who would be a suitable bone marrow donor [the process would not harm the new baby [saviour sibling].
(chapter 4. Tip - benefit v harm. In what way can this harm?)

106   Should alternative or complementary therapies be funded by the NHS?
(page 117)

107   What is meant by alternative medicine?
(pages 117 and 118)

108   What is the difference between alternative and complementary therapy?
(pages 117 and 118)

109   What is vivisection? Should experiments on animals be allowed?
(page 119)

110   A senior colleague arrives on the ward smelling of alcohol and looking drunk; what do you do?
(pages 55, 79 and 92)

111   A friend admits to you that she is depressed and asks
you to prescribe some antidepressants for her. How do
you react?
(GMC guidance is that it is inadvisable to treat your own
family and freinds - think of the main ethical principles and
how it may be harder to follow them - chapter 4)

112   Is it right for doctors to treat their friends or family? In
what situation could it be acceptable?
(as above)

113   The number of organs needed for transplantation
far exceeds supply. How is organ donation decided at
present?
(pages 42 and 43)

114   There is an organ shortage, so do you think Britain
should change to an 'opt out' system of presumed
consent?
(pages 42 and 43)

115   Should a 50 yr old woman be allowed IVF treatment?
Should it be funded by the NHS?
(pages 83 - 89)

116   Have you come across any ethical problems in the
news recently?
(chapter 4 should help you discuss and present it)

The Knowledge

Graduate students

117   Why did you not choose medicine as your undergraduate degree?

118   What skills will you bring from your past experience?

119   What made you change your mind about your previous career and do medicine?

120   What put you off continuing in your previous career?

Oxbridge Interviews

Remember all the usual questions asked above in addition to those below;

121   This is a graph of life expectancy over the last 200 years. Explain why you think it looks the way it does. (page 102)

122   Draw a graph of blood levels of a drug if it is a] ingested orally b] injected. (page 102)

123   What evidence is there that mitochondria evolved from viruses? (DNA/RNA, ribosomes)

124   Draw a graph of the incidence of an illness that is spread by a virus that confers life time immunity to a person after infection against time in years. (page 102)

125   Draw a graph of the incidence of an illness spread by a virus that mutates rapidly and is seasonal.
(page 102)

126   This is the last injection against a serious illness. Who should have it me or you?
(pages 102 and 103)

127   How do you prove the River Thames exists?

128   If there was to be a nuclear holocaust which ten people would you take in the bunker with you?
(pages 99 and 100)

129   How would you weigh your head without chopping it off?

130   How would you explain a human to an alien?

131   Is there such a thing as race?

132   Should people be allowed to sell their kidneys?
(Think of the conflict of ethical principles in Chapter 4)

133   How many animals did Moses take on the Ark?

134   Should obese people have free NHS treatment?
(pages 88 - 90)

135   What is your favourite part of the human brain?

136   What happens when you drown?

137   Is it best to fill a fish tank with cooled boiled water after cleaning it or just use tap water before putting the fish back?
(think about oxyen levels)

138   How do doctors decide if someone is dead?

139   Are humans still evolving? How could evolution work in this country with the Welfare State?

Overseas Applicants

140   Why did you decide you wanted to study in Britain?

141   What do you know about the NHS?
(chapter 3)
142   How is health care funded in your country?
(chapter 3)
143   Tell us about common health problems in your country
(compare with information in chapter 3)

144   How do social inequalities affect health care in your country?
(compare with information on page 66)

145   You will be living alone far from home. How do you think you will cope?

Why this medical school?
146   So you wish to come to this medical school. Why?
(chapter 7)

147   What appeals to you about this course?
(pages 106 - 108)

148   Why do you think PBL would suit you?
(pages 106 - 108)

149   Why do you think a traditional system of learning
would suit you best?
(pages 106 - 108)

150   What do you know about this medical school?
(chapter 7 and look at our facebook page)

151   What sorts of patients and illnesses do you think you
will see if you come here?
(page 66. Medical Schools are often situated in cities
with a mixture of the rich and poor with more immigrant
populations than the country as a whole)

152   What are the advantages and disadvantages of small
group leaning?
(pages 106 and 107)

153   How will studying medicine at University differ from
studying for your 'A' levels?
(page 108)

154   What have you done to find out about this medical
school?

155   Do you have any questions you would like to ask us?

Join us on facebook

facebook.com/MedicalSchoolInterviews

Contents include; topical issues discussed as they come up, a weekly ethical scenario and much, much more!